EXPERIMENTS WITH STEAM

EXPERIMENTS WITH STEAM

Landmarks in unusual British locomotive design 1846-1959

CHARLES FRYER

PSL

Patrick Stephens Limited

Front endpaper *A photograph of a painting by E.W. Twining of one of the ten Crampton locomotives built for the South Eastern Railway in 1851, in which inside cylinders drove cranks on a jack-shaft that was coupled to the driving wheels. They were eventually rebuilt as 2-4-0s. (NRM)*

Title page *No 10000, Gresley's high-pressure water tube boiler 4-6-4 as completed in its original form, with corridor tender. (NRM)*

Rear endpaper *No 6399 in the yard outside the works of the North British Locomotive Company, Glasgow, immediately after construction and before its ill-fated test run of 10 February 1930. (Mitchell Library, Glasgow)*

First published in 1990

British Library Cataloguing in Publication Data
Fryer, Charles
Experiments with steam: Landmarks in unusual British locomotive design, 1846–1959.
1. Great Britain. Steam locomotives
I. Title
625.2′ 61′ 0941

ISBN 1–85260–269–4

Patrick Stephens Limited, part of Thorsons, a division of the Collins Publishing Group, has published authoritative, quality books for enthusiasts for more than twenty years. During that time the company has established a reputation as one of the world's leading publishers of books on aviation, maritime, military, model-making, motor cycling, motoring, motor racing, railway and railway modelling subjects. Readers or authors with suggestions for books they would like to see published are invited to write to: The Editorial Director, Patrick Stephens Limited, Thorsons Publishing Group, Wellingborough, Northants, NN8 2RQ.

Patrick Stephens Limited is part of the Thorsons Publishing Group, Wellingborough, Northamptonshire NN8 2RQ, England.

Printed by Butler & Tanner, Frome, Somerset
Typeset by Burns & Smith Limited, Derby

1 2 3 4 5 6 7 8 9 10

Contents

Acknowledgements

My thanks are due to all who have allowed me to quote from books and magazine articles and to reproduce diagrams and drawings therefrom. I am also grateful to the staff at the Library of the National Railway Museum, York (NRM), and the Mitchell Library, Glasgow, for the opportunity to browse through published and unpublished material and to select illustrations from their archives. In particular I would single out Mr Nicholson, of the Mitchell Library, who was enormously helpful in providing material for Chapter 17.

The usual and the exceptional

When one turns the pages of a book of illustrations of steam locomotives built during the earlier part of the nineteenth century one is easily moved to mirth. Very high chimneys with tops like trumpets, domes resembling pepper-pots or tea-urns in almost any position on top of the boiler or firebox, front buffers made of padded leather which when up-ended would make good piano-stools (some later did), fireboxes externally resembling huge immersion heaters, wheels with spokes so thin that they look as if they would have snapped on a rough patch of track, cylinders pointing obliquely downwards from mid-smokebox or mid-firebox level, frames that overhung several feet beyond the leading wheels, inverted external springs looking like albatrosses about to take wing — one could go on at length about these early peculiarities that now seem so incongruous. But this would not be fair. Locomotive engineers were learning as they went along, feeling their ways towards common, acceptable and efficient norms. They were also limited by the qualities of materials available to them and by the unsophisticated techniques of their time. It was to be the same later when automobiles and aircraft developed. The surprising thing is that their early creations worked as well as they did and that serious accidents were not more frequent.

If all Chinamen look alike (a statement no Chinaman would make), all steam locomotives certainly did not, even after earlier eccentricities had given place, as the century wore on, to a generally recognizable shape. As with the human face, general likeness was associated with special individual features. Individual designers tended to build engines which bore a family resemblance to one another, even when they moved from company to company. Men trained at a particular locomotive works tended to regard its traditions, practices and productions as the best possible and, if one of them were promoted to a top job in another company, equally applicable there. Also, if one worked under a respected chief locomotive superintendent, one might, if appointed to succeed him, continue his designs with minor changes.

Hence by the end of the nineteenth century a general pattern of steam locomotive for fast passenger work was coming to predominate, albeit with regional differences. This was the inside-cylindered, simple-expansion 4–4–0, with a steam pressure of 160–180 lbs per square inch, a boiler of moderate size, a round-topped firebox, a fairly tall chimney, a dome of about chimney-height half-way between the smokebox and the cab front, a safety valve a little in front of the latter or else surmounting the dome, coupled wheels of from 6½ to 7 feet in diameter with large splashers covering their upper portions, connecting rods and valve gear between the frames, the drive being to cranks on the front-coupled axle set at right angles to one another, a cab of adequate and sometimes of generous size, and usually a six-wheeled tender exteriorly sprung. The whole ensemble was sleek in appearance, with few external excrescences and, when painted in a colourful livery and kept clean, good to look at.

Thus, round about the turn of the century the British express passenger locomotive achieved a brief moment of artistic perfection before the introduction of heavier trains, often running to brisker schedules, made further changes necessary. Longer and fatter boilers then began to appear, with shorter chimneys and squatter domes. The need to have three or four cylinders to achieve a greater tractive effort brought two of them outside the frames. Smokebox fronts began to protrude forward so as to leave room within for superheating equipment and other structures. Belpaire-type fireboxes became more common and often took the places of round-topped ones when older engines were rebuilt. Some lines, notably the Great Northern, adopted the 4–4–2 'Atlantic' wheel arrangement for their principal express passenger engines. The Great Western, on the other hand, after experimenting with 'Atlantics', went over to the 4–6–0 type for its chief express trains, and even built a solitary 4–6–2 'Pacific' which was too large to be used anywhere except between London and Bristol. After the First World War had ended still further enlargement was seen. The London, Midland and Scottish and the London & North Eastern railways developed 4–6–2s that looked even more enormous than the Great Western's experiment in that direction. Chimneys and domes became smaller and squatter, and with the building of streamlined engines on the LMS and line railways, and air-smoothed ones on the Southern, they disappeared from sight altogether. Boiler pressures rose to maxima of 250 lbs per square inch, sometimes even to 280. Running plates were raised until all or nearly all of the coupled wheels were visible. The later engines increased in mass and majesty but lost their former magic; Bonnie Prince Charlie gave place to Henry VIII. With the standard types from 1951 onwards, apparent (though not actual) top-heaviness and the open display of working parts became the family characteristic of engines that were intended to be utilized all over the British Railways' system. Then, suddenly, came the end of steam, the extinction of the dinosaurs.

So much for the general trend of locomotive design. This book, however, deals with particular engines that, so to speak, left the herd, exhibiting unusual features which their designers wished to try out and which they deemed desirable. Sometimes one solitary example was built, sometimes a few, sometimes many, before the special characteristic or characteristics incorporated into them were considered not worth perpetuating. This did not necessarily mean that the engines did not work well; Sir William Stanier's 'Turbomotive' was highly successful, as also was O.V.S. Bulleid's 'Q1' freight locomotive — the only one of the experimental locomotives considered in this book of which a surviving example remains, on the Bluebell Line in Sussex.

Very often what one Locomotive Superintendent thought to be a good idea, worth multiplying, did not commend itself to his successor, who either scrapped or rebuilt what he inherited. Locomotives did to a considerable extent express the likes and dislikes of designers — even what Rous-Marten called their 'fads'. So that one can at once say, 'This was a Stirling, this a Drummond, this a Churchward, this a Robinson product'. That is one reason why their study is so fascinating. Some of the experiments described in this book passed from the scene more or less unmourned, though one would like to have had some of them preserved. Ironically it was the ugliest of them all which had that privilege.

It is not claimed that the examples given in this book are all that could have been given. I have chosen some which particularly interested me. Some, like Stroudley's front-couplers and Bulleid's 0–6–0s, were successes. As to the others, W.H. Auden's lines seem applicable:

'History to the defeated
May say, Alas, but cannot help or pardon.'

2

The British Crampton locomotive

One problem, or what appeared to be a problem, which faced early locomotive engineers was that of retaining stability when an engine moved along a curved track at speed. The higher its centre of gravity, the more likely it was, when going round a curve, to tilt outwards and so bring about an accident. The tilt would not need to be more than a couple of inches for the wheels traversing the inside of the curve to lift their flanges so far that they were clear of the rail altogether. Furthermore, the locomotive would then be leaning some inches to one side and might strike an obstacle which it would normally have missed. Later experience has shown that early fears were exaggerated; the degree of cant now given to curved track is not so much to obviate danger as to make the ride more comfortable for passengers. In the Advanced Passenger Train, whose further development has now, sadly, been discontinued, extra tilt over and above the cant of the rails was given to the coaches through a special system of levers, so that curves could be comfortably taken at higher speeds than those previously stipulated; only the motor vehicle in the centre of the train was not devised to tilt, and as the actual driving was done from one end or other of the rake of coaches, neither passengers nor train crew would, it was hoped, have suffered any discomfort.

Another problem, also related to the locomotive's centre of gravity, was how to ensure that the pull from the engine's drawbar, exerted in line with the couplings between the hauled vehicles, was as far as possible also in line with that centre of gravity. If the centre of gravity was too high, tensions would be set up in the structure of the locomotive and some of the pull would be wasted. Ideally, it was felt, the centre of gravity should be in line with the drawbar and couplings when the train was travelling along a straight and level track. Was it possible to achieve this desideratum? If not, how nearly could it be approached in practice? Since the heaviest part of a locomotive was the boiler, kept filled with water nearly to the top when in action, it seemed desirable to find a way of lowering its centre line.

Thomas Russell Crampton, an inventor who flourished during the middle years of the nineteenth century, had his own ideas about how to overcome these two related problems. He had had railway experience, since he had worked at Swindon on the construction of engines for the broad gauge Great Western Railway. With rails 7 feet apart, a Great Western locomotive travelling along them was much less likely to get into unstable equilibrium when rounding a curve (though the question of whether the drawbar pull was in line with the couplings and the engine's centre of gravity was of course still there). The Great Western never had recourse to the expedients which Crampton devised after he left its service, but they impressed a number of other railway companies. In 1842 he took out two related patents, one for an engine whose boiler was placed *under* the axle of the main driving wheels, the other for one in which the driving axle was behind the firebox.

The first and more radical solution was tried out in 1847 by Francis Trevithick, who was then in charge of the railway works at Crewe. He constructed a 2-2-2 locomotive in which large driving wheels with a diameter of 8 ft 6 in permitted the placing of the boiler under their axle. It was in fact found necessary to make a channel across the top of the boiler in order to make room for the driving axle, while the axle of the rear carrying wheels had to be enclosed within a tube which went right through the firebox from one side to the other. The cylinders and motion were at a higher level than the boiler, in line with the centres of the driving wheels. No photograph of this astonishing object is known to exist, and perhaps none was ever taken, but drawings were kept of it as it was originally built, with only two front carrying wheels. An extra pair, it would seem, were added soon after, and the locomotive was exhibited at the Great Exhibition of 1851 in Hyde Park as a 4-2-2. There are no records to indicate its ability to haul trains. In 1858 John Ramsbottom, Trevithick's successor at Crewe, rebuilt it, and when he had finished there was not much left of the original machine apart from the wheels. The rebuild had a boiler conventionally placed above the driving axle and looked very much like other London & North Western 2-2-2 single-wheelers (for it had now reverted to its first wheel arrangement) such as Ramsbottom was then building. It had a long active life, and in later years hauled the Chief Mechanical Engineer's saloon coach. It appeared at the Liverpool and Manchester Railway's Centenary celebrations at Rainhill in 1930 and is now preserved in the National Railway Museum at York.

Crampton's second solution received expression in a number of locomotives on several British railways, but nevery really caught on in this country, whereas on the Continent, and especially in France (as will be mentioned later) much use was made of it. The first Cramptons to appear were built in England for a foreign line, the Liège and Namur Railway in Belgium. In these prototypes the axle of the single driving wheels extended right across the enginemen's footplate and was covered by a raised casing. It had of course to be simply a straight axle — there could be no question of room being made for cranks and eccentrics, the only possible places for these being at the axle-ends. So a locomotive of this type had necessarily to have outside cylinders and outside eccentrics to operate the valve gear. To improve stability, the cylinders were placed well back on either side, and set between the two front carrying wheels, which latter were not in a bogie but set in the main frame. The fireman had to shovel coal through the firebox door across the top of the driving axle casing, which must have taken some getting used to.

The boiler was a circular drum pitched low; the firebox was only 2 feet from front to rear. A dome with a shape somewhat reminiscent of a circular classical Greek temple, surmounted by a Salter safety valve, put out a separate steam pipe on either side, each leading directly down around the boiler cladding to one of the two cylinders. From each cylinder a straight pipe carried the exhaust steam forward into the smokebox, which was a little wider than the boiler but scarcely as long from back to front as the diameter of the base of the chimney. The front and rear carrying wheels were spaced well apart to allow room for the cylinders. Since the boiler was pitched unusually low, the front buffer-beam had to make a U-turn downwards between the buffers to allow room for the smokebox door to open.

A drawing of Richard Trevithick's Cornwall, *as first built in 1847, the boiler being slung beneath the driving axle. It was exhibited at the Hyde Park Exhibition of 1851 and rebuilt in 1858.* (Bracken Books, London)

The engine's most bizarre feature, however, was perhaps, the springing of the driving wheels. A single long transverse leaf spring, bolted in the middle to the back of the firebox, took the pressure of the driving wheel axle on either side through pillars which came vertically upwards from the bearings. The oval fire door was between this spring and the driving axle casing. As with most locomotives then built, there

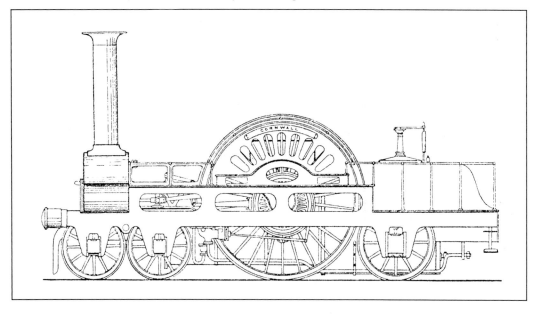

was no shelter for the crew. The builders of these prototypes were Tulk and Ley, of Whitehaven, Cumberland.

This first pair of Cramptons underwent tests on the main line of the London & North Western Railway before being exported to Belgium, and must have made a favourable impression since that company then decided to experiment with a Crampton itself. In November 1847 one was built at Crewe, but differed in some respects from those that went to Belgium. It had a boiler of elliptical section, strengthened inside with transverse stay-rods and pressed to 90 lbs per square inch; thus it was possible to lower its centre line. The firebox top rose well above that of the boiler, and steam was collected from its upper space as well as from inside a dome further forward. The *Courier*, as it was named, was not in all respects a success. It ran steadily enough, thanks to its low centre of gravity, but it was rough on the track. Tulk and Ley were therefore asked to provide another Crampton, which differed from the earlier one in detail. It had driving wheels 8 feet in diameter, larger cylinders, an elliptical boiler pressed to 100 lbs per square inch and a much greater heating surface. It was named *London* and worked between that city and Wolverton. Before being handed over it was sent for trials on the straight and almost level line between York and Darlington, and while on the way to its testing ground it had the misfortune to foul part of a station platform with its outside valve chest. It was, however, not derailed, which spoke well for the stability of the design.

Cornwall as rebuilt by John Ramsbottom at Crewe in 1858. It retained its large driving wheels and part of the framing but was otherwise a quite different locomotive. It worked express trains, on its own or as a pilot engine, until the beginning of the present century, after which it was used to haul the Chief Mechanical Engineer's saloon coach. It is now preserved at the National Railway Museum. (LCGB)

The London & North Western ordered yet another such engine, a sort of 'Super Crampton', in 1848. Daniel Gooch, who was in charge of the Great Western Railway's works at Swindon, had claimed that only on a wide gauge such as that of his own line — 7 feet — could a locomotive be made large and powerful without having too high a centre of gravity. His 4–2–2 engines were the largest of their kind in England at that time. Alexander Allan, now in charge at Crewe, believed that on the narrower standard gauge a locomotive equal in power to any of Gooch's monsters could be run, and yet be equally stable. His *Liverpool*, a 6–2–0, built by Bury, Curtis and Kennedy, was a prodigy; had he lived then, the cartoonist Heath Robinson, famous for his pictures of imaginary mechanical contraptions in the 'twenties and 'thirties of this century, would have revelled in contemplating its eccentricities. It was double-framed; the six front carrying wheels took by far the greater part of the engine's weight; its elliptical-section boiler was pressed to 120 lbs per square inch; its total heating surface was an astonishing 2,290 square feet; it had a wheelbase of 18 ft 4 in. The cylinder valves were operated by enormous eccentrics whose sheaves were 2 ft 9 in across and which were fixed outside the bosses of the driving wheels. There was no dome; instead, steam was taken to the cylinders from a 'regulator box' with a flat top and sides through very wide pipes around the sides of the boiler. In order to be in line with the centre of the rear driving wheels, which were 8 ft across, the cylinders were positioned above the outside frames. There were two fire-doors and two fire-grates divided by a longitudinal mid-feather. The front buffer-beam was curved downwards in the middle to such an extent that no central coupling would be fixed to it; instead, a chain was festooned between two ring-bolts fixed a little inwards from the front buffers. The splashers over the driving wheels did not more than cover their tyres and rims.

Liverpool, the 6-2-0 Crampton locomotive, built for the LNWR in 1848 and exhibited with Cornwall at the Hyde Park Exhibition of 1851. It was capable of hauling heavy trains but eventually had to be taken out of service because it damaged the track.
(Bracken Books)

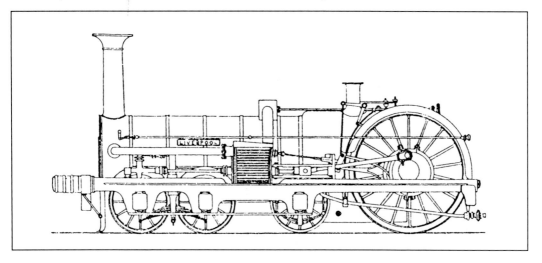

A painting of this locomotive is reproduced in C. Hamilton Ellis's book *Some Classic Locomotives*. He had to work from drawings as no photographs existed, and he admits that the tender is somewhat conjectural. *Liverpool* is shown standing in Coventry station (where in actual fact it would seldom have been seen since it usually plied between London and Wolverton) and is painted in red and brown, with a brass regulator box and safety valve cover and a splendid chimney with a copper-capped bell-mouth. The visible cylinder is painted bright red and has the London & North Western coat of arms on its side; a long tail-rod protrudes from its front end.

In 1851, *Liverpool*, like *Cornwall*, was displayed at the Great Exhibition, standing alongside the Great Western single-driver express engine *Lord of the Isles*, and the two vied with each other for public admiration, as did *Caerphilly Castle* and *Flying Scotsman* at the British Empire Exhibition at Wembley three-quarters of a century later. As a flag-carrier for its line, *Liverpool* was a great success; as a means of hauling trains it was less so since its long wheelbase and (for those days) great weight damaged the wrought-iron track. It proved itself able to pull up to 40 four-wheel coaches over the easy grades between London and Wolverton at the moderate speeds then customary, and was rumoured on one occasion (certainly not with 40 coaches) to have attained a maximum speed of almost 80 miles an hour.

In 1848 two Cramptons were built for service on the Midland Railway by Kitson, Thompson and Hewitson. These, unlike previous examples of the type, each had double framing extending the whole length of the engine, which gave them a very massive appearance. Between the inner and outer frames on either side were cylinders inclined slightly downwards, fed with steam from pipes which led from a dome half-way along the boiler. Dome, however, is scarcely an apt word for describing this object's appearance; it was a cylinder having a shallow square box for a base, with what resembled a chimney emerging centrally from its top (this contained a safety valve). Each driving wheel had a bearing on the inner frame and a journal on the outer, the former taking most of the weight; between each bearing and journal was a crank that took the big end of a connecting rod. The larger front carrying wheels and the driving wheels had external springs above the axles (so that the expected huge lateral spring behind the firebox was not required) but the smaller carrying wheels beneath the piston slide rods had inside bearings only and inside springs; they were made small to keep them clear of the reciprocating parts. A whistle projected from the summit of the firebox which, as in all Crampton engines, was short from front to rear.

Some Scottish lines also experimented with Cramptons. A single example, very similar to the ones built for Belgium, was constructed by Tulk and Ley in 1848 for the Dundee, Perth and Aberdeen Junction

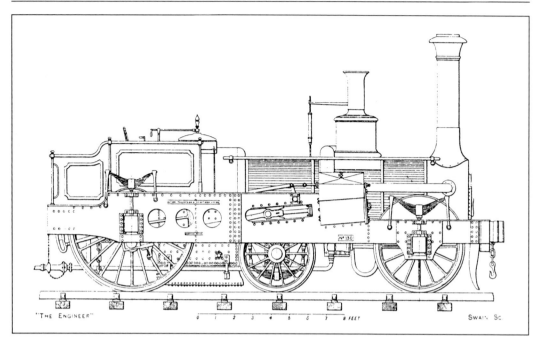

"The Engineer"   0 1 2 3 4 5 6 7 8 FEET   Swain Sc.

One of the two Crampton locomotives built for the Midland Railway in 1848. It was unusual in having double framing throughout its whole length, with both inside and outside springs for each driving wheel.
(Bracken Books)

Railway, soon to merge with the Caledonian; it was named *Kinnaird*. One photograph of it exists — the only one of a British-owned Crampton so far as is known — a bearded driver posing with his fireman on the footplate. It resembled the Liège and Namur Railway Cramptons (so far as one can tell by comparison of the photograph with a drawing) in every respect except in having a spectacle plate which could offer a certain minimal protection from the rigours of the Scottish climate. Later on, in 1850, the same company bought two more Cramptons, possibly cheaply since they had been part of a cancelled order from abroad, from the firm of E.B. Wilson, but no details are known about these.

In 1848 this latter firm had constructed six others, five of which had gone to the Eastern Counties Railway in England. Of their subsequent career nothing is known, but the sixth, purchased by the North British Railway, achieved a measure of fame when it hauled back to Edinburgh the train which had carried Queen Victoria to Berwick-on-Tweed to open the Royal Border Bridge south of the town. A coloured plate of this engine, which was painted in Royal tartan colours to commemorate its special claim to fame, can be found in C. Hamilton Ellis's *Four Main Lines*. It shows the splendid chimney with its copper-capped bell-mouth, the regulator box on top of the boiler crowned by a shallow convex eminence reminiscent of the familiar top of a municipal gasholder, the cylinders and ends of the connecting rods within the double framing and the shining brass splashers covering the rims of the driving wheels. Above and behind these the engine crew, without

benefit of cab or spectacle plate, appear to be admiring stooks of corn in an adjacent field as the train of dark red, flat-topped coaches runs near the North Sea east of Dunbar. A peculiar semaphore signal of ancient design indicates that the line is clear by being set parallel to the rails.

The South Eastern Railway also acquired three Cramptons, built by Tulk and Ley in 1947 and more or less similar to *Kinnaird*. No pictures of them exist and it would seem they did not have a long life. However, the South Eastern did somehow or other obtain other Cramptons, and mystery shrouds their origins. It rather looks as if they were rebuilds from existing South Eastern engines. The only hard evidence as to what they looked like is a water-colour painting by a Victorian artist E.W.Twining, based on a blue print he had somehow or other obtained. It depicts two locomotives which differ in detail, and neither of them could have been from the same stable as *Kinnaird* since the boiler mountings are quite different. Using an old outline drawing to guide him, Hamilton Ellis also painted a picture, reproduced in black and white in *Some Classic Locomotives*, of one of the two types shown by Twining hauling a train past an oast-house near Marden on the South Eastern main line to Dover. It has an enormous drum-like dome only a few inches to the rear of the chimney, and the buffer-beam is straight, whereas its counterpart in Twining's picture definitely has a downwardly-curved one. Ellis had also given his locomotive a spectacle plate, whereas Twining has not. But these supposedly rebuilt engines were not necessarily all exactly alike.

Kinnaird, built in 1847 for the Dundee, Perth and Aberdeen Junction Railway, on which it ran until 1854. So far as is known this is the only existing photograph of a British Crampton locomotive. (Dundee District Library)

The last Crampton of the original type, with outside cylinders, was a 4–2–0, generally resembling the two engines which had been sent to Belgium, and from the same makers, which was sold to the Maryport & Carlisle Railway in 1854. It did not last long in its original form, being rebuilt as a 2–2–2 six years later. It was possibly constructed from left-over parts from a cancelled order and may have been sold at a bargain price.

So much for what may be termed the Mark I Crampton type. But while engines of this sort were being built, Crampton himself was already designing a variation, and in 1849 he took out a patent for a new style in which the driving wheels were operated indirectly from inside cylinders through a jack-shaft coupled on either side to the driving axle through a connecting rod — rather as if the engine were a four-coupled one with the leading coupled wheels missing. In 1851 both the Great Northern and the South Eastern Railways acquired some of this type, which were domeless and had the firebox casing flush with that of the boiler. The Great Northern appears to have had only one, with driving wheels of 6 ft 6 in diameter; the South Eastern, on the other hand, had ten, with 6 ft drivers. The rear wheels were sprung in the same manner as those which had gone to Belgium, with a transverse spring across the footplate. Setting the cylinders between the frames meant that a low-slung boiler could not be used since it had to be high enough to clear the cranks on the jack-shaft. The boiler, too, was circular rather than elliptical in section. In fact, the supposed advantage of building the Crampton type was now lost, since the centre of gravity was as high as in any other type of engine. Not surprisingly, therefore, the Mark II

A photograph of a painting by E.W. Twining of one of the ten Crampton locomotives built for the South Eastern Railway in 1851, in which inside cylinders drove cranks on a jack-shaft that was coupled to the driving wheels. They were eventually rebuilt as 2-4-0s. (NRM)

design did not become popular. Only one other British company, the London, Chatham & Dover, ordered any, and these differed from all earlier Cramptons in two respects. Each had a front bogie instead of four carrying wheels supported in the framing, and the driving axle went beneath the firebox, not across the footplate. They were built in 1862 and had a short life in their original form, all being rebuilt within a few years as 2–4–0s or 4–4–0s.

No other Cramptons were built for service in Great Britain. It was otherwise, however, on the Continent. As this book is confined to British locomotives, a mere mention must suffice of the successes abroad of this prophet-without-honour in its own country. For some years, from 1849 onwards, engines of this design were built in considerable numbers for service on the Nord and Paris-Lyons-Mediterranean railways in France. Later on the East railway built some, and for over a quarter of a century the type reigned supreme on Paris-Strasbourg expresses. *Prener le Crampton* became a common French expression for 'to take the train'. These French engines lacked whatever grace the British ones might have been held to possess; they were covered with bits and pieces. However, they did their jobs well, or so many would not have been built. On them, too, some consideration was shown for the comfort of the enginemen, proper cabs being supplied. A number of German companies also used this type. On the Continent it was usual to press the boiler to a higher degree than in Britain, which may in part account for their greater success there than here.

In general, Crampton may be said to have achieved his aim of designing stable and steady single-drivers with low-slung boilers. The type's chief defect was its limited adhesion weight. When trains were lightly loaded this did not matter so much, but as they became heavier, greater adhesion was necessary, so his engines were all either scrapped or reconstructed. Even the mighty *Liverpool's* driving wheels only pressed down on the rails with a weight of some 12 tons, whereas a single-driver of the more usual 2–2–2 wheel arrangement, with the driving axle under the boiler, could manage a much better factor of adhesion. Patrick Stirling, on the Great Northern, was to get as much as 20 tons' adhesion weight with his later enlarged 8-foot singles. In France, the difficulty of inadequate adhesion was to some extent overcome by the simple expedient of placing extra weight beneath the footplate; in this country it was preferred to discard the type altogether.

Three breeds of 4-2-4 tank engines

Eight very unusual tank locomotives were constructed by Messrs Rothwell, of Bolton, Lancashire, during 1853–1854 for the broad gauge Bristol & Exeter Railway, the designer being that company's Locomotive and Wagon Superintendent, J. Pearson. E.L. Ahrons refers to them as 'the boldest departure made up to that time from the accepted canons of locomotive design, other than perhaps Trevithick's *Cornwall* and Crampton's *Liverpool*'. They appear to have been the first tank engines to be built in Britain which were intended to haul express trains. They had had precursors; an experimental 0-4-0 was made by a private builder in Birmingham round about 1837; two 0-4-0 well tanks appeared on the Dublin & Kingstown Railway a little afterwards; and ten years later three most unusual-looking 4-2-2s were built for service on the Waterford & Kilkenny Railway, which had side tanks running the entire length of the engines. In 1848 the London & Blackwall Railway also took delivery of some 2-2-2 well tank locomotives with outside cylinders. However, none of these was intended for fast running, which Pearson's engines definitely were, as the size of the large single driving wheels makes plain. They differed from all previously built locomotives in having flangeless driving wheels 9 feet in diameter, two four-wheel bogies, one before and one behind, of equal sizes, and springs for the wheels made of rubber.

Why Pearson adopted this wheel arrangement is not known. E.L. Ahrons thinks that he might have been aware of the views of Benjamin Cubitt who, in 1845, when he has Locomotive Superintendent of the Brighton, Croydon & Dover Joint Committee, had told the Gauge Commission, 'I think the driving wheels may soon get too high for safety, except you have plenty of other wheels to keep on the road with. You may get the driving wheels of any height .... If there are ten wheels it would perhaps be all the better. Two fours on bogie frames and a pair of drivers would be a very safe carriage.' This was what Pearson produced.

A supplement to *The Engineer* of 16 December 1910 shows diagrams of one of these peculiar locomotives. The first thing that strikes the eye is the supporting arrangement for the driving wheel springs (see the accompanying reproduction). On either side of the boiler cover, in line with the driving axle, two huge brackets project whose ends take the whole weight of the driving wheels, their axle and all the latter's attachments. At the upper and outer ends of each pair of brackets are holes through which a rod passes. Each rod bears a lever with two arms which project laterally, in line with the axle below, for a few inches. Jointed to the end of each lever-arm is a rod which descends towards the axle and terminates in a cylindrical brass casing which has within itself a kind of circular metal-and-rubber sandwich that reaches to the top interior of the casing. Shocks from the rails were absorbed by the rubber discs in the sandwich. There were four of these devices, two to each driving wheel. The arrangement looks so flimsy that one would have thought the rods above and below the brass casings would have buckled on slight provocation, especially when one bears in mind the fact that contemporary metallurgy was not yet up to producing the hard, tough

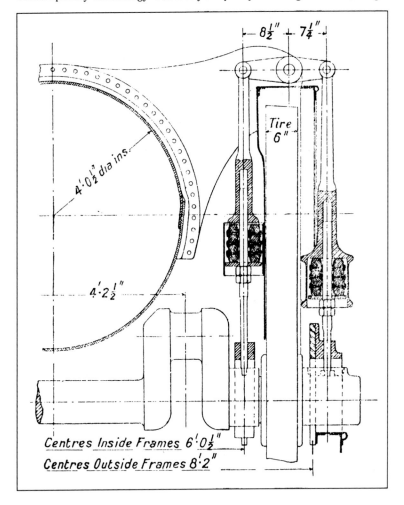

Diagram showing the rubber springing above the driving axle of Pearson's first 4-2-4 engine. It will be seen that the weight was taken by the boiler and not by the frame of the engine. (Bracken Books)

The Bristol and Exeter's 4-2-4 tank locomotive No 44, one of eight constructed to the design of J. Pearson by Rothwell of Bolton. Note the huge flangeless driving wheels, the canister and the end of a vertical rod within which were rubber springs controlling the axle's up-and-down movement, the brackets projecting from the side of the boiler and the widely spaced inside cylinders projecting forwards below the smokebox. (NRM)

steel which it became possible to make in the later years of the century. However, there is no indication that any of these locomotives was put out of action for such a reason. If one asks why such a method of springing was thought necessary, instead of the usual plate springs attached to the frame, the answer would appear to be that the engine's frames were much weaker than was common. The inside plate of the frame on each side was only 8 inches from top to bottom, except where it widened to take the driving horn-blocks, and it only extended as far back as the firebox, to the front of which it was riveted. The structure of the firebox and of the rear tank under the bunker was supposed to be rigid enough to serve as a continuation of the frame and to support the rear bogie.

Another well tank was placed just below the firebox and yet a third beneath the boiler just behind the rear axle of the front bogie. Room had to be made for the latter, so the cylinders, piston rods, connecting rods, cranks, eccentrics and valve gear had to be well away from the centre line of the engine, with consequent extra strain on the bearings of the driving axle. As the description of the latter's springing given above will have indicated, there were inner and outer bearings at each end of this axle, the outside ones being sited in triangular upward projections from the running plate. The enormous driving wheels had very narrow splashers which covered just over half of their rims. The cylinders were peculiar; they were neither wholly inside nor outside the frames, they were spaced well away from each other and their front portions projected well forward from the base of the smokebox.

The front and rear bogies were also unusual. They had large wheels whose axles had rubber springs below them, rods from which reached up to the bearings in a manner similar to the driving wheel arrangement, except that the strains and stresses were carried in the opposite direction. The bogies had ball-and-socket pivots exactly halfway between the axles. In the case of the front bogie, the ball portion was fixed to the lower surface of a winged casting fixed to the undersides of the cylinders; in the case of the rear bogie it was attached to the underside of the well tank beneath the bunker. The front bogie had horizontal stay-rods fixed to the engine frame to prevent it from derailing, but the rear bogie lacked any such precautionary measure.

The boiler was rigidly attached to the inside frames by means of large brackets similar to those from which the driving axle's spring support rods depended, but projecting downwards and outwards instead of upwards and outwards. For a broad gauge locomotive it was rather narrow, only just over 4 feet in diameter and 10 ft 9 in long. It had 180 fire tubes, each interiorly just under 2 inches wide. There was no dome, steam being collected from a perforated pipe along the inside of the top of the boiler. The safety valve was above the firebox, there was no cab and the whole locomotive in working order weighed 42 tons.

Details of how it performed on the road are very few; the practice of train-timing had not yet begun. A contemporary writer on railway matters, Mr Z. Colburn, said that these engines rode very smoothly; Ahrons was rather sceptical about this. One wonders what its haulage capacity may have been. The tractive effort cannot now be ascertained since no record has survived of its working pressure, but with cylinders 16½ in by 24 in and those enormous driving wheels it could not have been very great. Much of the Bristol and Exeter main line is fairly level, but west of Taunton it is a different story; Whiteball summit needs to be surmounted and the minimum speed at this point must always have been pretty low. There was, however, a rumour that one of them once touched 80 miles an hour descending from Whiteball. No 42 once suffered an unfortunate accident which was in no way due to its unorthodox construction; it was standing at signals in front of its train at Weston Junction when a train from Weston-super-Mare ran into its rear. The front carriage of its own train rode up on its coal bunker and buckled it inwards. For some reason not immediately obvious — perhaps it was the overriding coach — the brass safety valve casing also tilted forwards. Otherwise it does not seem to have been badly damaged, despite the weak framing.

However, the class could not have been found entirely satisfactory, since their replacement began in 1868, new engines with the same wheel arrangement taking their places and their numbers over the following five years. These were built at the Bristol and Exeter's works at Bristol just before that line was absorbed into the Great Western system in 1875. Perhaps 'replacement' is not quite the right word, since parts of the old engines, the driving wheels in particular, were used in the new ones. These latter had larger cylinders, 18 in by 24 in, set closer to each other; the old driving wheels were turned down to diameter of 8 ft 10 in, a slightly longer boiler was provided and both firebox and smokebox were somewhat enlarged. Entirely new framing was provided and the rubber springing was discarded in favour of conventional plate springs on all wheels. The front ends of the cylinders no longer protruded through the base of the smokebox. The two four-wheel bogies had slightly shorter wheelbases, the coal bunker was shorter but deeper, and a cab (without sides) was provided for the protection of the crew. The firebox contained transverse water tubes, foreshadowing Dugald Drummond's later practice on the London & South Western. The total weight was nearly 50 tons, of which 18½ tons rested on the driving wheels.

In this form they lasted until 1876, but during that year one of them ran off the rails near Flax Bourton. The reason given was that the permanent way was in an unsatisfactory state, but it is significant that the whole class was now withdrawn and rebuilt into 4-2-2 tender engines by the Great Western, which had now taken over the Bristol &

Bristol & Exeter 4-2-4 tank locomotive No 40, one of four built to replace the earlier engines built by Rothwell and also designed by J. Pearson. The rubber springing previously used was now replaced by plate springs above each axle, the single driving wheels were 2 inches less in diameter and end-to-end frames took the whole weight of the engine, no projecting brackets from the boiler being necessary. (NRM)

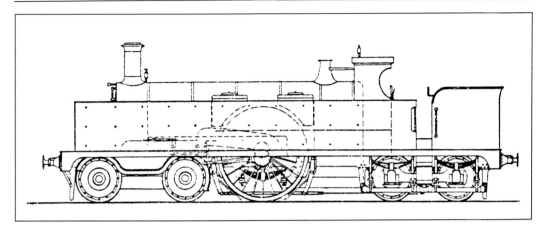

Exeter line; they were now given standard 8 ft driving wheels. Possibly it was felt that the weight on the 8 ft 10 in drivers of the tank engines had been excessive and that this had contributed to the mishap. In their rebuilt form they lasted until the broad gauge was abolished in 1892.

A drawing by E.W. Twining based on descriptions given to him of William Dean's ill-fated 4-2-4 tank engine, of which no diagrams were made or photographs taken. (David & Charles)

The last 4–2–4 tank engine to traverse Great Western metals appeared in 1881. William Dean, Locomotive Superintendent at Swindon from 1877 to 1902, had succeeded to his Chief, Joseph Armstrong, on the latter's death. He was only 37 at the time, and the world seemed to lie at his feet, for he was both intellectually brilliant and very hard-working. In his time he was responsible for some very handsome locomotives which peformed as well as their splendid appearance promised — particularly the 4–2–2 singles, one of which made a record run from Bristol to London in less than 100 minutes — a few complete failures, and one which never had a chance even to fail, and whose story is about to be related. It was built during the fourth year of his superintendency, and had a shorter life than any other locomotive which ever left any British railway workshop.

The engine in question was No 9, a large tank locomotive 36 feet in length from one buffer beam to the other, and with single driving wheels 7 ft 8 in in diameter — which suggests that, like its Bristol & Exeter predecessors, it was intended to be used on fast trains. It was built for the standard gauge. The water supply was partly from a well tank, and partly from side tanks which extended from the cab, which was open at the back, to a point some 4 feet in front of the smokebox door. A brass safety valve cover surmounted the firebox which was flush with the top of the boiler. There was no dome. A moderately-sized coal bunker covered the rear well tank. Inserted within each sidetank were sandboxes on either side of the driving wheels, with exit pipes directed to deposit sand on either side of them. There were inside cylinders, of dimensions now unknown. The link motion and eccentrics were outside the wheels and drove slide valves above the inside cylinders by means of rocking shafts. Of the bogies (in designing which for other locomotives Dean was frequently to go wildly wrong) no details are known beyond the fact that they had Mansell-type wheels with solid wooden blocks between the hub and the rim. The front bogie must have had interior springing; the rear bogie had outside plate springs. The smokebox carried a neat chimney with a copper-capped mouth, and a whistle perched on top of the cab.

The time came for the new engine to emerge from the works at Swindon. The Revd John Gibson, who worked at Swindon in his youth and was able to talk to eyewitnesses of the event, had described in his *Great Western Locomotive Design: A critical appreciation* what happened on that inauspicious day:

> 'It is related that the great man himself (for William Dean was very much the Victorian potentate at whose approach everyone trembled) came down from his eyrie to watch the "engine of the future" steamed and brought out of the shops for the first time. In the works yard there stood a turntable, conveniently sited for engines entering or leaving the erecting shops. This "masterpiece" managed, just, to get as far as the turntable, then derailed and tumbled into the pit. Dean is said to have turned and walked away, leaving his underlings to cope with the crisis. It is generally believed that this engine never did get as far as the main line. A number of Dean's designs were given to de-railing .... but this was the worst of all. It never stayed on long enough to get anywhere. With no fixed wheelbase at all, and the rear bogie almost completely uncontrolled anyway, it is strange that anyone should have expected it to have any sense of direction, and stay on the track. It didn't.'

A veil of silence descended on both event and engine. Anyone inquiring after this locomotive was met with a polite admission of ignorance and told he must be thinking of the old Bristol & Exeter tanks. The reason why anything is known about it at all, once the records were (presumably) destroyed, is that its general appearance was reproduced in a line drawing by a railway artist, who gathered his information from those who recalled the catastrophe and were prepared to spill a few beans. Somehow or other it was salvaged. All the king's horses and all the king's men managed to get Humpty Dumpty back into the works, where it was covered with tarpaulins to hide its shame from every eye. Parts of it were later included in a newly built 2-2-2.

4

Sturrock's steam tenders

A steam locomotive suffers from the inescapable handicap of having to carry around with it the dead weight either of a wheeled tender or of water tanks and a coal bunker in order to have continual access to fuel and water — something which its diesel-driven equivalent requires only in part and its electric equivalent not at all. Towards the end of his superintendency at Doncaster works on the Great Northern Railway, it occurred to Archibald Sturrock that, though this dead weight could not be dispensed with, it could in a freight locomotive be made to contribute to the latter's wagon-hauling capacity by making use of its weight for adhesion and, in effect, turning it into a second engine by fitting it with a separate installation of cylinders, piston rods, connecting rods, cranks and valve gear, steam being supplied by a pipe from the locomotive's boiler. In this way an 0–6–0 engine could be converted into a 0–6–6–0, and all 12 wheels would be able to grip the rails without an excessive load being laid of the track at any single point. This was an important consideration on the Great Northern at this time, since its track-bed was still to a large extent laid with rails that were light and weak. One could not gain extra adhesion simply by piling extra weight on the wheels of the locomotive alone and expecting to avoid accidents due to rail breakage.

Sturrock was not the first railway engineer to have this idea. There had been experiments as early as 1843 in central France with steam-propelled tenders, on the line between Lyons and St Etienne where heavy coal trains had to be hauled. Benjamin Conner, on the Caledonian Railway, also briefly fitted four 2–4–0s with steam tenders. Both experiments, however, were tentative and short-lived, whereas Sturrock seems to have meant to go in for them in a big way. As things turned out he did not remain long enough to establish them as a regular feature on the Great Northern.

In May 1863 he took out a patent for such a tender and, having the facilities of Doncaster works at his disposal, began to experiment. Taking an existing spare tender, he reconstructed it by installing two 12 in by 17 in cylinders between the frames, about 4 feet from the front end and level with, but just to the rear of, the foremost axle. These operated two cranks set at right angles to one another on the middle axle, which also held the eccentrics that worked Stephenson's valve gear. All six wheels were connected on either side by coupling rods external to the framing. Whereas before conversion the wheel centres were equidistant, in the reconstructed tender the middle axle had to be placed nearly a foot further back to allow enough room for the motion. The cylinders received their steam by means of a pipe from the rear of the steam dome of the engine which led backwards along the top of the boiler, curved over and ran vertically down the rear of the firebox, turned back beneath the footplate to pass under the locomotive's drawbar, and finally made first an upward and then a downward curve before entering the steam chest between the tender cylinders. It was jointed in five places to allow the slight necessary movement without the escape of steam. A separate reversing lever fixed on the tender's front operated the latter's valve gear, and the dome of the engine itself had two regulators, the foremost one controlling steam supply to the locomotive's cylinders, the rear one that to the tender. The locomotive was modified to receive an extra long firebox, in the hope that the boiler could thereby be induced to raise sufficient steam for all four cylinders.

Once steam had been exhausted from each tender cylinder it passed into condenser units, of which there were two extending longitudinally along the floor of the tender tank. Each unit consisted of 15 long tubes, sloped slightly downwards towards the rear and fixed at either end into a box-like container; the front one received the steam and passed it into the tubes, while the rear one passed it into a wide copper tube that led vertically upwards into a chimney. Just below the top of the latter a baffle-plate, and an inverted cone with its apex cut away, interposed themselves to catch any uncondensed steam before it could escape into the atmosphere — though in fact some always did escape. Thus, when working, steam would be seen rising from three chimneys, one at the front of the locomotive which also took away the products of combustion, and two at the rear of the tender. The two sets of tubes, 30 in all, were in contact with the water in the tender tank. It was expected that most of the exhaust steam from the tender's cylinders would

An original drawing, produced at Doncaster works, of Sturrock's goods locomotive with steam tender. Slight differences appear from the drawing shown on page 32; the latter was the design put out for tender, the former was the locomotive reconstructed at Doncaster. (NRM)

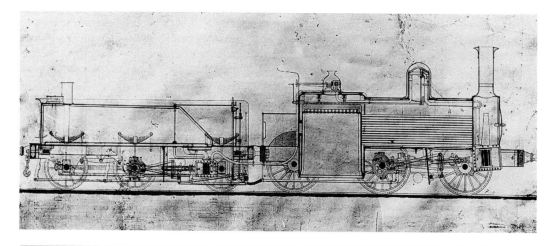

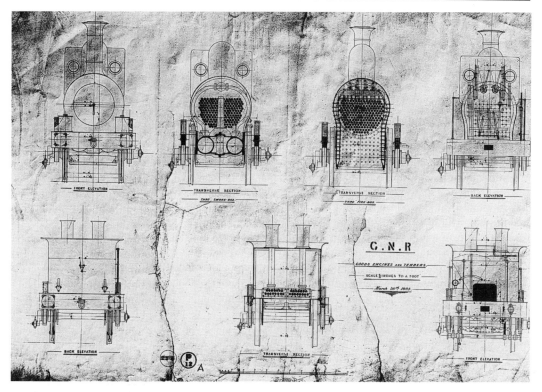

G.N.R

GOODS ENGINES AND TENDERS

SCALE ½ INCHES TO A FOOT

March 30th 1869

Cross-sectional views of Sturrock's reconstructed engine showing details of its structure. (NRM)

condense and supplement the water in the tank, either in the tubes or when striking the inverted cones and baffle-plates before falling back into the tank.

Having taken out his patent and seen for himself his device at work, Sturrock now entered into negotiations with the Board of his own Company and a certain amount of turkey was talked. In the end the directors agred to pay him, in respect of each steam tender, half of what would be due from any other line which might adopt his invention, up to a maximum of £50. It was now in Sturrock's interest to get as many built as possible. Some 30 were constructed at Doncaster during 1864–1865 on the pattern of the prototype, some having 4 ft 6 in coupled wheels, others 4 feet only. Contracts were also given to the firms of Hawthorn and Co and Kitson and Co for each to build ten engines complete with steam tenders.

By the beginning of 1866, 50 complete units were at work and more were on order. A sort of 'triangle of forces' now began to form. Sturrock had a financial interest in getting as many built as possible and contemplated the construction of as many as 210. His reports to the Board of Directors were carefully phrased to convey the impression that all was well and that performance was satisfactory. *Per contra*, the footplate men who actually had to use the things became increasingly disenchanted with them and resented being obliged to work them, for reasons that appear below. As for the Board itself, its members wished to know the true facts and be sure that they were not throwing money away, and they seem to have become suspicious after rumours reached them from the Running Department that all was *not* well. When Sturrock asked for permission to have more built, the question was deferred. To use an expression which has recently gained currency, they were beginning to think that he had been economical with the truth. It was at about this time that the object of their distrust came coincidentally into a fortune and resigned his position on the railway, retiring to enjoy life of a country gentleman and sit as a local magistrate until increasing deafness made it impossible for him to follow what was said in Court. He survived to be 94 — the longest-lived locomotive superintendent known to history. He had served the Great Northern well in the past and it was a pity that he had to leave under a cloud.

The specification for each new steam tender, issued when offers were invited from firms wishing to build them, and signed by Henry Oakley, then the Company's Secretary and later its General Manager, makes interesting reading, and a few extracts are quoted below. The printed requirements reflect existing engineering practices and their limitations, and one notes the insistence on certain kinds of material being used. The tender's cylinders were to be of metal

'.... so hard as to be with difficulty bored, and to be perfectly free from honeycomb, solid and sound throughout. The valve faces are to be planed perfectly level and scraped, so as to have a true and steam-tight facing .... The piston and rod to be forged on one solid piece and made of the very best scrap iron .... The outside frames to consist of wrought iron plates with wood packing between. The wood to be dry and well-seasoned X American oak, 3½ in thick by 10 in deep. The plates on each side to be of good Staffordshire iron, seven-sixteenths of an inch thick .... The tires to be carefully expanded by heat and shrunk on to the rim of the wheel by being suddenly cooled in water. Great care to be taken that all the wheels are the same diameter. The whole of the tender to be painted with three coats of the best mineral paint and well rubbed down. The tank sides to be painted Brunswick green and panelled, similar to those now in use on the Great Northern Railway. The frames to be painted brown, and the whole afterwards to have three coats of the best coachmakers' varnish, and to be well rubbed down after the first coat of varnish has been laid.

Along with the specification and detailed drawings went an outline drawing of the complete locomotive and tender, suitably lettered to correspond with the items in a descriptive panel, and with a scale which showed that the complete engine was 25 feet in length and its tender 21 ft 6 in, the coupled wheelbases being 15 ft 8 in and 15 feet respectively. The engine's firebox was 6 ft 9 in long and sloped very steeply downwards across the rear coupled axle. The steam pipe leading from the regulator in the dome to the tender's cylinders was 3 in wide. The engine's coupled wheels were 5 ft in diameter, those of the tender 4 ft. Their cylinders were respectively 16 in by 24 in and 12 in by 17 in. The engine in working order weighed 33 tons, the tender 29 tons (the latter figure would of course decrease in the course of a journey as coal and water were used up). An interesting feature of this diagram, which bears Sturrock's signature, is that the descriptive panel is repeated in French. This was because contracts for construction were sought from a French engineering company as well as from firms in Great Britain. The French offer, being too high, was not accepted.

Sturrock must have felt chagrin during his retirement at the fate of his steam tenders, which began to be converted into ordinary six-wheeled tenders within a year of his departure. Patrick Stirling, who came from the Glasgow & South Western Railway to succeed him at Doncaster in the summer of 1866 found an atmosphere of disgruntlement prevailing there, and was himself not well pleased with much that he found on entering office. In November 1866 he made a report to the Board of the Great Northern on the performance of the steam tender units, and this ended any expectation that they might constitute a solution to the problem of how to haul heavier freight trains. He had ordered an enquiry to be made into their behaviour and a number of facts had come to light.

In the first place, they were highly unpopular with the men who had to drive and fire them, and who were in effect being required, for the same wages, to look after two locomotives at once. The work of the fireman had been much increased, while the driver had a second set of controls to operate and twice as much oiling to do. In the course of a journey, the footplate became insufferably hot; the back of the firebox was radiating more heat, the steam pipe supplying the tender's cylinders was adding its quota, while behind something like an enormous kettle was coming to the boil. It was expected, of course, that the water in the tender tank would rise *somewhat* in temperature, through transference of heat from the condensing steam; in fact, it heated up so much that it failed to do any condensing after a certain time. So, while the men on the footplate were sweltering like the meat in a toasted sandwich, clouds of steam were rising from the two vertical chimneys at the rear of the tender and preventing them from keeping a proper watch down their train of wagons. The consequence was that little things were always going wrong. Leaking tubes, in particular, called for almost daily repair. Furthermore (though this did not appear in the report) footplatemen were not above a little discreet sabotage now and then in order to get the hated tenders removed from service for a while.

Stirling disliked them as much as his enginemen did, and when he put out his report he accompanied it with figures that were quite damning. The new tenders were supposed to have made for more economical working. Certainly they would have obviated some piloting, but at huge cost. He tested out five of them against five other 0–6–0s of similar locomotive size, and found that the steam tender units consumed much more fuel and oil than those with conventional tenders. The long fireboxes gave out so much heat that the water in the boiler could not absorb it all; when it was running, therefore, the draught pulled so much heat through the tubes into the smokebox and chimney that the latter often became red hot, hence the high rate of fuel consumption. Furthermore, when the units were running light or going downhill, the additional power was not required, the tender, whose

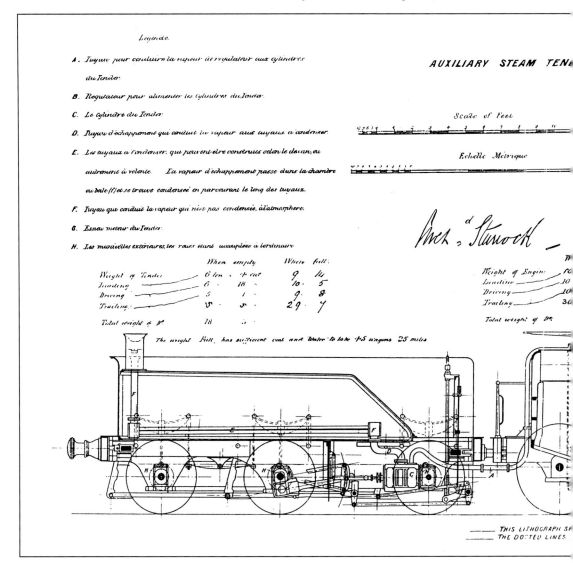

weight was almost as great as that of the engine, still had to be dragged along, with the consequent wear and tear to its mechanism. When repairs became necessary to the tenders, their locomotives had to remain out of service.

The Board accordingly made up its mind to end the experiment, the clinching evidence being a communication from the Running Department reporting the reactions of the footplate staff, about which Sturrock had said nothing. One firm which had almost completed five new engines with steam tenders was asked to modify the latter, removing the redundant machinery; another, whose ordered

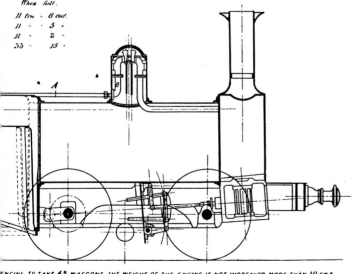

Description.

A. Pipe for conveying steam from the regulator to Tender Cylinders.

B. Regulator for supplying steam to the Tender Cylinders.

C. Tender Cylinders.

D. Exhaust pipe for conveying the steam to the Condenser.

E. Condensing apparatus, which may either be made according to the design, or to any other plan if preferable.

The exhaust steam enters the chamber or box (f) and condenses whilst passing along the tubes.

F. Pipe for conveying the uncondensed portion of the steam into the atmosphere.

G. Tender crank axle.

H. Outside Cranks, the wheels being coupled in the ordinary manner.

When full.

11 ton	8 cwt.
11 "	5 "
11 "	2 "
33 "	15 "

ENGINE TO TAKE 45 WAGGONS, THE WEIGHT OF THE ENGINE IS NOT INCREASED MORE THAN 10 CW⸴
D⸴ 30 D°

A facsimile of a drawing, signed by Archibald Sturrock, of his 0-6-0 goods locomotive with steam tender. Note the jointed pipe by which steam was supplied to the tender cylinders. (The Engineer) locomotive were not so far advanced in construction, was simply asked to substitute ordinary tenders. As for the ones already at work, these were altered as quickly as possible. One supposes that Sturrock had already received the agreed royalty payments for them, as well as for six which the Manchester, Sheffield & Lincolnshire had ordered, to help him to maintain his new life-style as a country squire.

In retrospect one is disposed to reflect on what might have happened if Sturrock had not had his windfall and had remained in office. Teething troubles are the lot of any locomotive innovator. Some form of heat-shield could perhaps have been placed in the locomotive cab. The tender cylinders might have been reduced in size. Perhaps an air-blower could have been installed, worked by hand from the footplate, to ensure that from time to time a rearward view could be obtained along the train of wagons. As to the discomfort suffered by the men on the footplate, perhaps they could have been offered a 'steam tender bonus', analogous to 'danger money'. (This, however, would probably have been anathema to the economic thinking of the time.) In regard to wear and tear, perhaps some free-wheeling device could have been contrived which would switch out the reciprocating parts when their efforts were not needed. Certainly Sturrock had every inducement to make sure that his invention was a success. As it was, fate removed first himself and then his steam tenders from the railway scene.

It does appear, too, as if the Board never cottoned on to the deliberate sabotage that was being practised. Possibly there was a conspiracy of silence at lower levels. In those days there were no strong trade unions to take up the complaints of men who were expected to work in intolerable conditions and drive two engines at once, and one may allow oneself some sympathy towards their stratagems. Quite likely Patrick Stirling knew what was going on, and looked the other way; in this matter, though he could not have admitted it, he would have been on the men's side.

5

Stroudley's front-coupled express engines

If, after due thought, to attempt something that no one had attempted before can be deemed an experiment, William Stroudley, Locomotive Superintendent on the London, Brighton & South Coast Railway, was certainly experimenting when he brought out a new pattern of express locomotive which aroused the prophets of doom to forecast disaster. It had neither a leading bogie nor a pair of forward carrying wheels, yet it was intended to haul the principal express passenger trains between London and the South Coast. No other line ever contemplated using a locomotive with the 0–4–2 wheel arrangement for such a purpose. To do such a thing, it was held, was to invite accidents through derailment.

The reasoning behind such criticism can easily be appreciated. Consider a locomotive travelling along a curved track. The ups and downs of its reciprocating machinery affect the downward pressure on each driving wheel, which is not constant but continually fluctuates. If a locomotive with front-coupled wheels (or front single driving wheels, for that matter, if such an express passenger engine can be imagined to exist) were to enter a curve at speed, and if the moment of entry on to the curve were to coincide with a point of minimum weight on the outside front wheel, there might be a risk that centrifugal force — the tendency of an object moving in a straight line to continue in the same direction — would be enough to make it mount the rail, the sideways pressure of the wheel-flange not being enough to prevent it. If the engine were also 'nosing' slightly, such a movement outwards from the centre of radius of the curve, coinciding with a moment of minimum weight on the rail, would increase the risk still more. Given sufficiently high speed, poorly maintained permanent way and the circumstances indicated above, any locomotive of whatever kind might be derailed.

However, if the locomotive's driving wheels are preceded by a four-wheeled bogie, or even a two-wheeled truck which has limited sideways movement controlled by springing, the case is different from what it would be with leading driving wheels. When the truck or bogie reaches the entry to a curve, since it is not rigidly attached to the whole engine frame but is on a pivot so that it can point in a different direction on either side, the latter is indeed what happens. The springs controlling the bogie or truck, being compressed on one side and extended on the other, operate to push the wheels back to their central position. This they cannot do because the wheel-flanges bear against the rails, so the thrust pushes or pulls back in the opposite direction against the engine frame, nudging it slightly in the direction of the curve, and the driving wheels follow suit. Thus the latter follow the curve more easily.

Of course this depends on the truck or bogie being very carefully designed, and some locomotive engineers, notably William Dean in his early days as Locomotive Superintendent on the Great Western, had great trouble producing a bogie which would not derail. It was received opinion, none the less, among engine designers that it was a bad idea to put the coupled wheels right at the front. It was allowable in the case of locomotives which moved at slow speeds, such as goods engines or suburban passenger tank engines which made frequent stops, but not with express locomotives.

In this matter Stroudley was content to be heretical. The railway for which he worked had built-in limitations and he had to work within them. It was not a line on which racing could be performed, like the Great Western or Great Northern. There was little opportunity to attain high speeds when summits and depressions followed one another in quick succession (there were no fewer than three tunnel-crowned summits in the 40 miles between Croydon and Brighton on the main line). An 'express' on the Brighton line in Stroudley's day meant a train that might occasionally go above the mile-a-minute mark but would seldom if ever reach 70. In any case, his engines were supplied with speed-indicators (something almost unknown on other lines) to supplement the drivers' judgements.

A second limitation was turntable length. The available turntables were all too small to take a locomotive with eight wheels as well as its tender. All the locomotives with tenders which Stroudley designed were six-wheelers. But could not the turntables have been enlarged? Not so easily. The most critically-sited ones, such as that at Victoria, were in many cases hemmed in by buildings which would have had to be demolished first. So, if it were desired to introduce more powerful locomotives, while one could widen the boiler one could not greatly lengthen it or the frame on which it rested. There would not be room for a leading bogie. A two-wheeled front truck with four coupled wheels behind it would have meant that less of the engine's weight rested on the coupled wheels.

Having settled for the 0–4–2 wheel arrangement, Stroudley proceeded with caution. In 1876 he brought out a mixed-traffic engine, *Lyons*. (All the Brighton line's locomotives in his time were named, except for the goods engines, which were also in a different livery from the others, being painted in dark green instead of in the famous ochre-yellow set off against or lined out with six other colours.) He tried it out for six months before putting any others on the road. Apart from the wheel

arrangement there was nothing specially unusual about it. The huge wooden brake-blocks, which would have occasioned the raising of eyebrows in later years, were not unique; other Stroudley locomotives had them, in particular his 'D' Class tank engines, first built in 1873, parts of which were interchangeable with similar parts on *Lyons*. In fact, the latter was in nearly all respects a tender-attached version of the former.

During the six months' trial period nothing unfavourable was reported. The two duties Stroudley chiefly had in mind for it and its successors were the running of fast freight services containing perishables such as fruit from the South Coast to London and the *Grande Vitesse* freight service between Victoria and Newhaven which connected with the steamers across the Channel. These required to be punctual but involved no high speeds. Evidently *Lyons* proved its ability to run them, and a second such engine, *Caen*, joined it in 1877. Six more followed in 1878 and another half-dozen in 1883. In the latter, the wooden brake shoes were replaced by cast iron ones, and another interesting addition was what was called 'steam lubrication', applied to the rims of the front wheels. 'Lubrication' was a misnomer; what really happened was that, when the driver thought it necessary, steam could be released from the steam chest through a narrow copper pipe on either side of the engine to play upon the rims of the leading coupled wheel. By the time it had emerged from the pipes the steam had become hot water, which jetted against the flange and tyre in order to clean it

Stroudley's 0-4-2 No 305 Genoa of the 'Lyons' Class, with 5 ft 6 in wheels. Note the wooden brake blocks. The names chosen for these mixed-traffic engines had to be short in order to fit on the small wheel splashers. (NRM)

and so improve the adhesion of the wheels. This device was added to all subsequent Stroudley 0-4-2s. All 14 except one were named after Continental cities, towns or resorts, to which one could travel by way of the Newhaven-Dieppe steamer service. The exception was *Albion*, the poetic name for the country from which all such travellers would start.

The performances of *Lyons* and *Caen* encouraged Stroudley to build similar engines with 6 ft 6 in driving wheels, a foot larger than those of their predecessors. In 1878 the first of these appeared, *Richmond*. It was now that alarmist voices began to be raised. Wheels of this size obviously betokened express running, and it was true that Stroudley had one particular express train in mind — the 8.45 am business train from Brighton to London Bridge, which ran up in 70 minutes, slipping coaches at East Croydon for Victoria, to deposit its top-hatted and very important business magnates in the City. The boiler of *Richmond* was the same size as that of *Lyons*, but the heating area and cylinder volume were a little larger. To the eye the obvious differences were the larger coupled wheels, covered by larger splashers, and the slightly different shape of the sandboxes on the front splashers. As with *Lyons*, the dome was set well back on the boiler barrel. It was a very handsome locomotive. Once it had proved itself, five more were built during 1879–1880. They were named, in order of appearance, after three counties and two statesmen. The fourth to appear, *Beaconsfield*, was clearly named after Benjamin Disraeli, Conservative Prime Minister at the time and a great favourite with the old Queen, who conferred on him the earldom of that name. For a short while they were the principal express locomotives on the Brighton railway, until their more famous

Stroudley's 0-4-2 No 610 Belgravia (originally numbered 210 and named Cornwall), the longest-lasting of the 'Richmond' Class. Note that each driving wheel has a pair of cast-iron brake shoes, not the single wooden one as fitted in the earlier 'Lyons' Class. (NRM)

successors displaced them. They lasted for over 20 years before being withdrawn.

Train loads continued to increase and a larger version of *Richmond* was decided upon. Again Stroudley proceeded with circumspection, constructing just one to start with and then watching its performance very carefully. Mindful, perhaps, of having previously favoured the leader of one political party, he redressed the balance by calling the new engine *Gladstone*, who in 1880, as leader of the Liberals, had become Prime Minister for a second time. Criticism re-awoke; pessimists said Stroudley was asking for trouble, but he defended his decision in a speech made before the Institute of Civil Engineers. He had wished, he said, to give his locomotive adequate adhesion, and since an engine's heaviest weight was at the front rather than at the rear, that was where he had decided to put the four coupled driving wheels. A bogie would have been an unnecessary complication. There was also the turntable difficulty mentioned above. It had been contended that large wheels would tend to derail more readily than smaller ones. He did not agree. With a large wheel the flange on the outside of a curve came into contact with the inside of the rail at a greater distance in advance of the point of tread, so that a much greater force would be needed to lift it over the rail.

Gladstone was outwardly very similar to *Richmond*, but had a slightly longer and more highly-pitched boiler and cylinders an inch wider in diameter. For a whole year it remained the sole example of its class, while its designer followed its performance intently. He had specified that the tyres of the driving wheels should be made of very hard steel,

One of Stroudley's 'Gladstones', No 172 Littlehampton, *in its original condition and livery. These engines resembled the 'Richmonds' except in having somewhat larger boilers. No 172 has the continuous handrail along the boiler and smokebox installed by Stroudley's immediate successor, R.J. Billinton* (NRM)

'Gladstone' No 176, originally named Pevensey, seen in D.E. Marsh's umber livery, with the LB&SCR monogram replacing the name on the rear splasher. It will be noticed that the locomotive and tender only just fit the turntable. (NRM)

and he paid particular attention to the profile of the treads of the leading pair, watching to see how they wore. Eventually he gave the go-ahead for others to be constructed, and over the next eight years 35 more appeared. They were his supreme achievement, though he did not live to see the last half-dozen come out. It might even be said that one of them occasioned his own early death. No 189, *Edward Blount*, which was exhibited at the Paris Exhibition in 1889, was awarded a gold medal. Later it was sent, together with another British gold-medallist, 'F' Class 4–4–0 No 240 from the South Eastern Railway, to the main line of the French company which linked Paris with the Riviera, for high speed and heavy load testing. Stroudley accompanied it, caught a chill which brought on a severe attack of asthma, and died in Paris a few days later.

For 20 years the 'Gladstones' ran the chief Brighton line expresses. They were not immune from accidents, but in no case was any of these attributable to the design of the engine. When at length new 4–4–0s by Stroudley's successor, R.J. Billinton, began to replace them (for the turntable problem had now been solved) they were gradually moved to secondary services. In their heyday they kept the 70-minute timings between London and Brighton, sometimes with an intermediate stop, without difficulty. Occasionally one of these trains would have one of the new Pullman coaches included in its make-up, painted dark brown but elaborately lined out and lettered with gold leaf, with ordinary coaches in varnished mahogany, white-roofed and with vermilion ends, flanking it on either side. Engine and train together must have made a magnificent spectacle. If only colour photography had then been possible!

Both Billinton and his successor Douglas Marsh thought the 'Gladstones' worth rebuilding, though this was not so drastically done as to destroy their characteristic appearance. With Marsh they lost their gorgeous ochre livery and assumed the dark umber which replaced it, but they still looked good, even though many of them now lost their names. The first few to be withdrawn disappeared in 1910; the survivors proved their usefulness during the First World War and were eventually absorbed into the Southern Railway, some being painted in olive green. One by one they disappeared. *Gladstone* itself was purchased for preservation in 1927, and eventually found its way to the old York Railway Museum. It is now housed in the new one, where it vies for admiration with the equally beautiful 'D' Class South Eastern & Chatham Railway's No 737. The last to be withdrawn was No 172, which was also the last to have been built. So much for the honourable careers of a class which fully justified its designer's expectations, and which the dismal Willies had wanted to be strangled at birth.

One other type of 0-4-2 mixed traffic engine perhaps deserves mention alongside Stroudley's. On the London & South Western Railway, William Adams introduced his 'A12' Class with this wheel arrangement in 1887, the year of Queen Victoria's Golden Jubilee, the class accordingly being commonly termed 'Jubilees'. One has to suppose that the success of the 'Gladstones' had something to do with their appearance, though no one could have mistaken one of them for

A 'Gladstone' cab interior, showing the name of the regular driver, the dates of overhaul and the mileage covered between them. Allowing for withdrawals for routine maintenance, the figures more or less correspond with a daily journey of 100 miles, the distance from London to Brighton and back. (NRM)

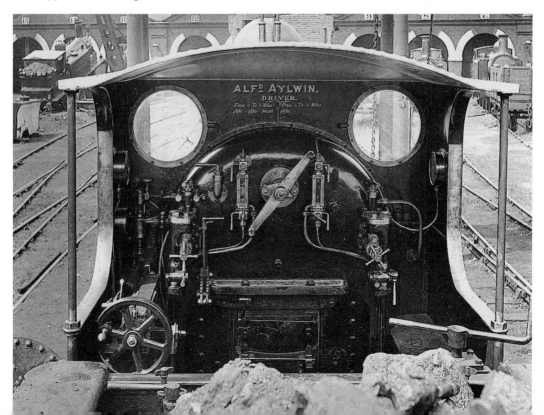

A 'Gladstone' photographed towards the end of the LB&SCR's separate existence, after modifications by both Marsh and Billinton, and now in umber livery, with a cast-iron chimney, a safety valve separate from the dome and a tender coping to retain more coal. (LCGB)

a Stroudley engine. The wheel arrangement was the same, and the sandboxes were similarly positioned, but the dome was further forward and the safety valve was just in front of the cab. The chimney, too, was a very poor relation of the Brighton line's copper-capped type — a mere stovepipe. For some reason Adams was partial to stovepipes, whereas his successor, Dugald Drummond, hated them, and when an Adams engine came in for heavy repairs it was usually given a more shapely Drummond built-up chimney. After the first 'A12' came out of Nine Elms works there was an interval; then it was followed first by nine more, then by 29 more, then by 40 further ones, and eventually by a final 20, so that the South Western had far more of this type than the Brighton line ever did. But they never achieved fame, though they were good work-horses. Another line that built quite a number with this wheel arrangement was the Caledonian, which in 1878 and again in 1881 bought some from Dübs and Company for goods traffic and used some of them for passenger traffic on the newly-opened Callander and Oban line for a while. They were ungainly engines, with outside cylinders and running plates curved over the wheel bosses; they had four sandboxes, two forward-facing ones on the front splashers and two facing rearwards on the rear splasher. Their chimneys were stovepipes and, when working the trains to Oban, were married to small four-wheeled tenders. Stroudley would have shuddered to see them.

6

Webb's three-cylinder compounds

Whereas the various locomotives so far described blossomed very briefly, the pattern of locomotive next to be described had a long flowering period and put forth a number of blooms one after the other. This was not because of its proved merits but because its designer chose for a long while to avert his eyes from its defects. Once he had vanished from the railway scene, his brain-children were all rapidly scrapped and there were many dry eyes when this happened. Not that the principle of compounding was itself misconceived; many successful compound locomotives were to be built during and after Webb's time, notably on the Midland Railway. Neither can Webb be blamed for making mistakes — all locomotive engineers have done so. But he was an obstinate man and persisted wrong-headedly in following a blind alley to its very end, as if he were quite unaware of the serious faults which the engines he designed displayed in practice. He went on tinkering with a general pattern which should have been discarded, until the London & North Western Railway was littered with his cripples — engines which, unless they were very lightly loaded, could be trusted to keep time only when piloted.

He reigned autocratically at Crewe from 1871 to 1903 — a very long innings indeed, only surpassed by that of Daniel Gooch on the Great Western Railway (if one includes the years spent as Director and Chairman of the company after he had resigned as Locomotive Superintendent at Swindon). Webb had his virtues. He reorganized Crewe works into an efficient concern capable of turning out half a dozen new locomotives every month, using assembly-line techniques similar to those employed in car factories. He was a prolific inventor of new devices for improving performance. His rebuilds of his predecessor Ramsbottom's 2-4-0 'Newtons', the famous 'Precedents', were perhaps the most successful passenger engines of their day; every railway enthusiast knows how No 790 *Hardwicke* covered itself with glory during the 'Railway Race' to Aberdeen in the summer of 1895. But consciousness of his own abilities developed into an assumption of his own infallibility. He came to assume that he was always right, and deeply resented criticism. Towards the end of his career this attitude came to border on insanity. H.A.V. Bulleid, in his entertaining book

Master Builders of Steam, relates a memory of H.G. Ivatt who accompanied his father to a dinner engagement at the house of George Whale, Webb's successor at Crewe, and listened intently as H.A. Ivatt (builder of the Great Northern 'Atlantics') and Whale talked about Webb's final days in office.

'Whale said that what precipitated the expected end was when Webb was shown a new drawing, to which he took an immediate dislike. He scribbled over it with a pencil held in his fist, tore it up, flung the pieces on to the floor and stamped on them. Too many of the staff witnessed this unfortunate scene. Whale, with the support of Trevithick and Bowen Cooke, went to Euston and reported to the Board that things could go on no longer in this way.'

Webb was a man who persisted in his mistakes, and it is possible that he was never aware of their extent, since no one dared to tell him. Hence the long sequence of unsatisfactory three-cylinder compounds, most of which to a greater or lesser extent gained a reputation for unreliability, so that the very word 'compound' became like a red rag to a bull for London North Western locomotive crews.

Compounding is a way of making the steam from a locomotive's boiler do its work twice over by exhausting it from one cylinder or pair of cylinders into another or others before its final discharge into the atmosphere. It was a method already being widely used in stationary engines and in steamboats where there was plenty of room for the extra appliances needed. Applying the principle to railway locomotion was another matter, since the loading gauge imposed restrictions. In theory, a single-expansion engine could be so designed and operated that the whole expansive force of the steam reaching the cylinders did work on the faces of the pistons. In late nineteenth-century practice this did not happen, and the front-end arrangements were often such that it could not happen. Some locomotive engineers were very much aware of this problem, notably Dugald Drummond. He was himself an opponent of compounding, believing that with proper driving methods any two-stage expansion was unnecessary. But getting drivers to work with a full regulator and to vary the cutoff as the road made necessary, so that the pressure on the pistons came chiefly from the expansion of the steam admitted to the cylinder, was something that even he, with all the force of his vigorous Clydeside personality, failed to achieve while he was in his own country, though he did manage to train the London & South Western enginemen into better attitudes. However, with compounding it was hoped by many of Drummond's contemporaries that the steam's expansive force would be used willy-nilly, the engine taking, as it were, a double gulp of each packet of steam, and that savings in the consumption of fuel would then result.

Quite a different number of cylinder arrangements were possible in a compound locomotive, even though the number of cylinders was restricted to between two and four. If there were to be three, there could either be a single high-pressure cylinder between the frames and two low-pressure ones outside, or the other way round. If there were to be four, two inside and two outside, either pair could be high or low pressure. Moreover, each cylinder did not *have* to drive on a separate crank, for it was possible to place high-pressure and low-pressure cylinders in tandem, operating a single connecting rod; in this way all could be inside the frames, and two British companies experimented with this method, as will be seen in a subsequent chapter. Another possibility was to have two cylinders only, to operate in compound once the locomotive was on the move but with high pressure steam in both cylinders when starting; the following chapter describes how this was applied by one locomotive engineer. A three-cylinder system with one high-pressure and two low-pressure pistons, with temporary admission of high pressure steam to all when starting or when extra effort was needed, as when climbing a steep bank, was used in the only compounds built in this country which operated so successfully that their numbers were greatly multiplied — the celebrated 'Midland Compounds' built at Derby by Johnson, Deeley and Fowler in succession. Webb, unfortunately, chose an unreliable method and persisted in it for many years.

His interest in compounding arose when a French railway engineer, M Mallet, displayed a compound tank locomotive at the Paris Exhibition of 1878; it had one high-pressure and one low-pressure cylinder, both outside the frames. Webb decided to experiment, and took an ancient 2–2–2 locomotive which, as originally built, had two outside cylinders 15 in by 20 in; he reduced the diameter of one of these and fed the high pressure steam into it, the other taking what it exhausted. It was put to work on light passenger trains on the branch from Nuneaton to Ashby-de-la-Zouch. According to Webb, 'elements of success were seen in its working', so he decided to go ahead and build a compound to his own design.

Evidently he was not much struck by the notion of two-cylinder compounding. Even before he had rebuilt the single-driver he had stated that a three-cylinder system would be preferable. In a discussion on the subject, when Mallet's design was under review by members of the Institute of Mechanical Engineers, he gave it as his opinion that 'the boiler steam should be taken into the middle cylinder first, and thence into the outside cylinders, which should have their cranks in the same position and at right angles to that of the middle cylinder'. This had been the arrangement adopted by Robert Stephenson when he had built a long-boilered, single-expansion, three-cylinder locomotive in 1847 for the London & North Western Railway; it secured that each double thrust, to and fro, of the outer pistons would complement a single thrust, to and fro, from the inside cylinder. Very careful calculation of relative cylinder capacities would be needed to ensure that the thrusts on the high-pressure and low-pressure pistons balanced one another, to give an approximately even torque.

The peculiar thing was that when the plans for Webb's first three-cylinder compound appeared on the drawing-board he was seen to have changed his mind. There were to be two high-pressure cylinders outside the frames and one low-pressure one between them, which meant that the latter had to be of very large diameter. Not only this, but he deliberately left the driving wheels uncoupled; the inside cylinder drove the front axle and the outside cylinders the rear. This certainly had the advantage of reducing the weight of the moving parts but, as will be seen later, it brought disadvantages at the same time. Another unusual feature was that the Joy's valve gear, which worked off the connecting rods, operated valves below the outside cylinders, not above them or to one side. This was because the valves had what were known as 'trick ports', which were pressed against the sliding surfaces when steam entered or left the cylinders by the pressure in the steam chest, but when steam was shut off they could fall very slightly away from that surface by their own weight and so reduce friction. The inside cylinder, on the other hand, had its ports in the conventional position above. Each high-pressure cylinder exhausted into an intermediate receiver, which took the form of a pipe four inches wide running round the curved interior of the smokebox in an up-and-down loop; from it the low-pressure steam chest was supplied, and the hot gases in the smokebox were employed to heat and dry the steam *en route*. Finally,

Webb's first 2-2-2-0 three-cylinder compound Experiment, built in 1882 then withdrawn and rebuilt soon afterwards with larger high-pressure cylinders since in its original form it did not have enough starting power. (NRM)

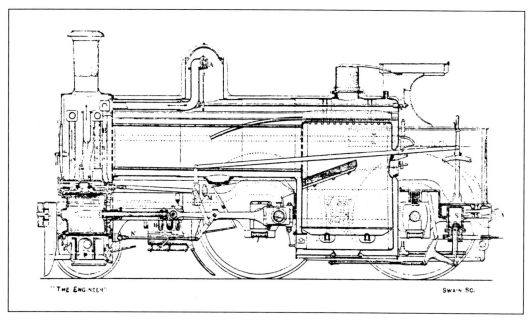

"THE ENGINEER"   SWAIN SC.

the exhaust from the low-pressure cylinder escaped through the blast pipe towards the chimney.

Experiment, as the locomotive was named, was built in 1882 and was then set to work between Euston and Crewe. It was used intensively, with two crews manning it alternately, but it was not extended by being given fast trains to haul. Most of its work was done on the more lightly loaded Irish Mails. In practice it did not prove satisfactory, as the high-pressure cylinders had been made too small (they were only of 11½ in diameter) and it was sluggish in starting. In its original form it had a short working life of only 12 months; it was then put aside for a while before being rebuilt to match its immediate successors.

Webb obviously considered that *Experiment* showed sufficient promise to justify other compounds being built. When he did this he made the outside high-pressure cylinders 1½ inches wider. He also fitted a relief valve to the inside low-pressure steam chest cover so that the maximum pressure in the inside cylinder could never exceed half the boiler pressure of 150 lbs per square inch. A third alteration was to arrange that steam could be admitted to the inside cylinder directly from the boiler at the driver's discretion. The declared intention was to enable the cylinder to be quickly warmed up, but drivers also used it to help the engine to start. This facility, however, had to be paid for by creating a back-pressure in the outside cylinders, so that much of what was gained on the swings was lost on the roundabouts. Twenty-nine of these engines were built, and were generally known as 'Compounds' after the name given to the first of the batch. *Experiment* was later rebuilt to match them.

These 30 engines were intended to replace the 2–4–0 'Precedents' on the company's principal express trains and were a little heavier. However, it was found that they were quite unable to do what the smaller engines were achieving. After a short while, therefore, they were relegated to light trains as soon as a larger and heavier class had taken the road. These latter were known as 'Dreadnoughts', again from the name given to the first of the class, and had the same general plan as the 'Compounds', but their boilers were pressed to 175 lbs per square inch, their high-pressure cylinders were an inch wider, and the low-pressure cylinder was increased in diameter to 30 inches, 6 inches more than the length of the stroke. The width of the driving wheels was lessened from 6 ft 7½ in to 6 ft 3 in. The 'Dreadnoughts' had a somewhat greater heating surface than their predecessors and weighed nearly five tons more. Surely, now, here were engines capable of out-performing the 'Precedents'.

Alas, not so. Starting was still a problem in spite of the increased diameter of all the cylinders. Webb therefore prepared yet a fourth design. He left the cylinder sizes unaltered and used the same-sized boiler, but he increased the diameter of the driving wheels to 7 ft 1 in.

The amount of the valve travel was also slightly increased. The greatest change was in the inside valve gear. In the previous classes it could be adjusted from the footplate, to vary the cut-off. In the new class seven out of the ten built were so constructed that this could not be done; the low-pressure cylinder always cut off at 75 per cent irrespective of how much the high-pressure cylinders might be notched up or down. Not only this, but the inside valve motion could not be put into reverse from the footplate either; it was worked by an eccentric which ran loosely on the driving axle and was pushed round by stops on one side of the crank web. When the high-pressure cylinders were put into reverse, the wheels they drove had to move backwards a full half revolution before the inside eccentric was forced by the stop to go into reverse as well — and vice versa. Thus a certain amount of moving machinery was obviated, and the system usually worked well enough, but (as will appear below) there could be awkward moments. Nevertheless, for some reason not fully understood, the 'Teutonics', as the class was known, again from the name given to the first, worked much more successfully and reliably than their 70 predecessors. Possibly the slight lengthening of the valve travel had something to do with it.

Ever the ingenious experimenter, Webb decided to attempt a triple expansion engine when building the third of this class. It was so constructed that steam passed from one cylinder to a second and then into a third before exhausting. It could also be worked by steam direct from the boiler to all cylinders if extra power were required. It could not have been a success, however, as no details were ever made known of its performance and it was soon rebuilt to match the other 'Teutonics'.

While these ten engines were better than those which had gone before them, they were by no means faultless. Webb had put a bypass valve in the receiver pipe to prevent steam from entering the low-pressure cylinder when the outside valve gears were put into reverse, and this was operated from the footplate by rod-and-lever mechanism. The latter would occasionally stick. Then, to quote E.L. Ahrons (*The British Steam Railway Locomotive, 1825–1925*, Chapter 18),

'.... this defect resulted on a few occasions in one of the funniest phenomena which ever occurred in locomotive working. When the engine backed on to a train ready for a start, the driver reversed the high-pressure gear, but the low-pressure eccentric remained in back gear. If the rails were dry and the high-pressure driving wheels could move the engine forward a few feet to revese the eccentric, all went well, but if the rails were greasy the high-pressure driving wheels spun round and filled the receiver with steam, which passed through the defective valve and, if one of the low-pressure ports was open, into the low-pressure cylinder, with the result that the middle or low-pressure driving wheels began to slip round in the opposite direction.'

Other untoward things could also happen. Again, to quote Ahrons:

Webb's 'Dreadnought' 2-2-2-0 three-cylinder compound No 2058 Medusa, photographed at Crewe. The front end of the inside low-pressure cylinder can be clearly seen below the smokebox door. Note the open top of the toolbox on the tender, from which the driver has presumably taken the oilcan he is using. (NRM)

A Webb 'Dreadnought' 2-2-2-0 No 2064 Autocrat. It appears to be in mint condition — but it was in fact about to be taken to Crewe for scrapping, in February 1905. Note the placing of the outside high-pressure valve beneath the cylinder, associated with 'trick' ports for admitting steam. (NRM)

A 'Dreadnought' piloting a 'Teutonic' at the head of a train on Castlethorpe troughs. (NRM)

'Frequently only one high-pressure cylinder was open to steam, the other being on dead centre and the ports of the low-pressure cylinder closed. In these circumstances it was obviously of no use to admit steam to the low-pressure steam chest, for when the high-pressure driving wheels slipped, as they almost invariably did, the high-pressure exhaust choked the receiver until the valve on the latter blew off, and the back pressure on the high-pressure piston stopped the slipping. If the engine managed to move a few feet and the low-pressure cylinder became open to steam, the receiver pressure diminished rapidly and the high-pressure engine started slipping again, and so on, alternately. Gradually some sort of equilibrium was established and the train moved slowly away. Very frequently the engine had to back more than once, and in the early days of the "Compound" class of 1883–84 the assistance of four men with pinch-bars was not unknown.... It was a serious defect, rendered worse by the use of uncoupled wheels.'

'Teutonic' No 1304 Jeanie Deans. For more than 8½ years this engine was rostered to work only two trains daily, the afternoon Scottish express from Euston to Crewe and its return counterpart, with loads varying between 250 and 300 tons. This was a heavy assignment in those days, but the time was consistently kept on a 50 mph schedule. (NRM)

To build locomotives whose separate parts played Laurel and Hardy with each other was certainly a sign of very exceptional genius — the sort akin to madness?

Webb's 'fad' (as the celebrated railway journalist Charles Rous-Marten termed it, when Webb was no longer in the saddle at Crewe — before then he had to watch his words as he depended on the Great Man for his footplate pass) of not coupling the driving wheels meant that the cylinders did not act together but independently, each working its own axle. Coupling rods would have enabled the high-pressure and low-pressure cylinders to co-operate. What in fact happened was that at low speeds a disproportionate amount of the work was done by the low-pressure cylinder, so that the pull on the drawbar was uneven and a

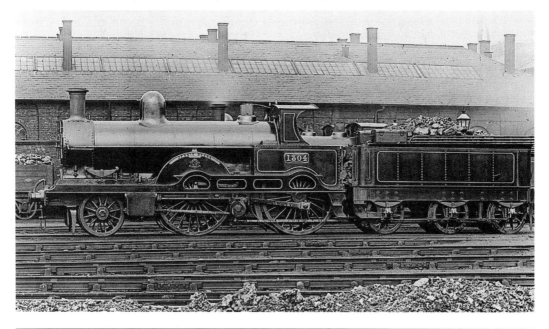

'Teutonic' No 1305 Doric
*hauling a train of three
GWR bogie clerestory
coaches and a mixed bag of
smaller coaches and vans at
Bayston Hill, near
Shrewsbury.* (NRM)

violent to-and-fro surge was felt throughout the whole train, to the great discomfort of the passengers. This gradually died away as the train gathered speed, and after a while it was the low-pressure cylinder's turn to take it easy, once the cut-off in the others had been reduced, since the pressure in the receiver was now lower and there simply was not enough steam to operate the central piston effectively. So on any given journey the potential pulling power of the engine was not used. Yet another disadvantage of not coupling the wheels was that the two systems got out of phase with one another.

Taken all in all, therefore, the earlier Webb three-cylinder compounds, including the 'Teutonics', were not consistently reliable. The surprising thing was that Webb went on to add to their number. Between 1891 and 1894 he built ten more express passenger engines, known from the name given to the first of their class as the 'Greater Britains', which were generally similar to the 'Teutonics' but differed principally in the following respects: the high-pressure cylinders were enlarged to a diameter of 15 in; Joy's valve gear was replaced by Stephenson's which was put inside the frames; much longer boiler was provided, with a combustion chamber between the front and rear tubed portions; and a pair of rear carrying wheels was placed beneath the firebox and cab, so that the wheel arrangement became 2-2-2-2. These engines were intended as, so to speak, 'Super Teutonics'. In fact they did not perform as well as their immediate predecessors. Finally, with the steep gradients of the Carnforth-Carlisle stretch of the main line in mind, he built ten versions of the 'Great Britains' with 6 ft 3 in driving wheels. These turned out, when sent to their intended running-ground, to be

complete failures; they were quickly taken off main line trains and scrapped a few years later. In regard to the 'Greater Britains', their combustion chambers (within which it is doubtful whether much combustion of unburnt gases really took place) were always giving trouble, and in spite of their size and theoretical power they needed to be piloted when hauling really heavy trains.

The three-cylinder compound saga ended in 1893 with the building of 111 0-8-0 goods engines. They had the same cylinder arrangement as the passenger types, but the wheels were coupled, the boilers were as long as those of the 2-2-2-2s but lacked combustion chambers, and all three cylinders were inclined at 10½ degrees to the horizontal. After Webb's retirement they were all converted to single-expansion working.

So much for the history of one of the most costly and ill-considered experiments that any Locomotive Superintendent was ever permitted to indulge in. After 1896 Webb himself seems at last to have seen the light; he went over to four-cylinder compounding, coupling the driving wheels. These later engines were more successful than their three-cylinder forbears (though by no means perfect) and were more conventional in design, so no account of them is included here.

A good deal is known of how the three-cylinder compounds performed on the road, thanks to the articles published by that indefatigable observer of locomotive running, Charles Rous-Marten. In the June and August 1901 issues of *The Railway Magazine* he gave a two-part account entitled 'What Mr Webb's Compounds have done'. They contain much apologetic comment; clearly he wanted to present these engines in as good a light as possible. A vein of special pleading runs through both articles. Rous-Marten affirmed that, whatever other people might have discovered, his own experiences had been generally favourable. He admits that the 'Experiments' (ie the 'Compounds' which included the rebuilt *Experiment*) were no longer equal to traffic requirements, but excuses them as having been designed for lighter and slower trains. He praises the 'Dreadnoughts', saying that they could run fast, but has to admit that they had difficulties when starting. He mentions a run behind one of them, *Raven*, on the '10 am Scotch Express' (it was usual then to refer to trains bound for Scotland as if they were whiskies) with a load of 190 tons; Rugby was reached in 83 minutes net from Willesden Junction (77.1 miles) and the subsequent 75.5 miles to Crewe were covered in 77 minutes, 'one of the smartest performances I have ever noted with the 'Dreadnought' compounds. Even a single performance such as this would suffice to establish the character of the "Dreadnoughts" for smartness and efficiency'.

In another run on the 10.30 am from Euston to Perth with 160 tons, *Achilles*, of the same class, covered the 90.1 miles from Preston to Carlisle, including the climb to Shap summit, in just over 100 minutes, the average speed from Tebay to Shap, a stretch that included four miles at 1 in 75, being 38 miles an hour. One may agree that this was 'smart' work, but no one need question that a skilful driver, with a locomotive in good condition, could coax good behaviour out of his charge, at some

2-2-2-2 three-cylinder compound No 1548 John Penn, one of the 'John Hick' Class, similar to the 'Greater Britains' but with smaller 6-foot driving wheels. Ten were built, intended for use on the heavy gradients between Carnforth and Carlisle, but they proved utterly useless and were soon taken off express services. (RM)

cost, no doubt, in coal. The driver, too, may very well have known that he was being timed. Even if Rous-Marten had not approached him at the beginning of the run, he was a familiar figure easily recognizable on station platforms, and the guard quite possibly told the driver, of this and many other occasions, that 'you know who' with the tall hat, tail coat and battery of stop watches was on the train. A dry rail and a following wind, too, could make a lot of difference when climbing Grayrigg and Shap inclines.

Rous-Marten's experiences with the 'Teutonics', too, had, according to him, been consistently favourable. He mentions *Jeanie Deans* in particular; with loads never less than 250 tons he had never in the course of many runs known this engine to lose time on the afternoon express from Euston to Glasgow, which it regularly hauled as far as Crewe. Once, with 326 tons behind it, it had only taken 101¾ minutes for the 91½ miles between Nuneaton and Willesden Junction, an average of almost 54 miles an hour. With such a load this was certainly creditable, and it is a pity that he gives no maximum or minimum speeds.

With the 'Greater Britains' he declared his experiences to have been uniformly good, and he noted an ability to attain speeds of 80 miles an hour on downhill gradients and sustain minima of 36 and 25.7 up Grayrigg and Shap banks respectively with loads of 170 tons. As to the 'John Hicks', the 6 ft 3 in 2–2–2–2s, he could say nothing either way because he had had no runs behind any of them which had not been piloted (a fact that should have made him suspicious, and perhaps he was, but he refrained from saying so). He sums up his experiences thus:

'I am offering an absolutely impartial and unprejudiced statement of what Mr Webb's compounds have done in a few particular cases under my own personal observation. What they could do then it is reasonable to assume they could do always *under identical conditions*.'

Fair enough, but it was not what they *could* do (if, for example, thrashed, or driven very skilfully) but what they actually did, day by day, over the years, that really mattered. Furthermore, once Webb had retired Rous-Marten was nothing like so complimentary about them. Two paragraphs from his May 1907 *Railway Magazine* article, written when Webb was safely in his grave, may serve as their epitaph:

'In the case of the Webb three-cylinder system, even apart from the self-evident hopeless inadequacy of the boiler power and steam pressure, the lack of wheel-coupling was a fatal flaw, in view of the necessary inter-dependence of the high-pressure and low-pressure action. The two sets of machinery were theoretically independent of one another, and yet each depended on the other. The low-pressure cylinder could not operate until it had received steam from the high-pressure cylinder. The high-pressure cylinder could not operate a second time until the low-pressure cylinder had consented to receive the exhaust of the steam used in the first operation of the high-pressure cylinder. Yet there was no means of absolutely assuring the synchronous working of the two. I pointed this out to Mr Webb so long ago as 1884, but he insisted there was nothing in the objection. Experience proved that there was *everything* in the objection. The frequent failure in synchronism rendered the three-cylinder compounds untrustworthy and often sluggish. Nevertheless I urged all that time back — 23 years ago — as I do still, that the plan, in spite of its manifest drawbacks, should have fair treatment and a thorough test. That particular plan has, I think, had a thorough test, and with unsatisfactory results, the outcome being that all of the 100 engines have been condemned, and most of them scrapped.

Yet these results were curiously various in detail. There has never been any doubt why the first (or "Experiment") batch of 30 proved failures. Apart from the non-coupling, the insufficiency of boiler and of steam pressure amply explained this. But the second batch of 40, with larger boilers, had far more promise of success, and indeed in some degree attained it. I have many notes of excellent work with engines of that class. Still, they were not trustworthy, but were always uncertain and often sluggish. The third batch, on the other hand, the "Teutonic" set, ten in all, were remarkably efficient, and very few indeed are their records of failure. It has never been clearly explained why this was so, or why the final batch of the three-cylinder compounds — the ten "John Hicks"— proved the most complete and unadulterated failures of all. That remains a Crewe secret and I shall not attempt to penetrate the mystery. The penultimate, or "Greater Britain" batch of ten might be classed with the "Dreadnoughts". They did much good work, and much bad, but like all the rest of the type — excepting perhaps the "Teutonics"— were untrustworthy. Thus only ten out of the hundred three-cylinder Webb express compounds could be characterised as fairly successful.

7

The Worsdell-von Borries two-cylinder compounds

Von Borries' 2-4-0 two-cylinder compound built for the Hanover State Railway. The pipe from the dome takes high-pressure steam to the right-hand outside cylinder; this in turn exhausts through a receiver beneath the boiler into the larger low-pressure cylinder on the other side. The small dome behind the huge main one contains sand to be fed under the rims of the front driving wheels. Notice the unusual design of safety valve, immediately in front of the cab. In the cross-section view the different sizes of the two cylinders can be appreciated. Because of loading gauge restrictions in Great Britain, T.W. Worsdell had to find a way of placing both cylinders within the frames. (The Engineer)

Francis Webb was the first British locomotive engineer to experiment with compounding in a big way. As already seen, he had very little success with his three-cylinder engines in the opinion of all who had anything to do with them, apart from himself. Later experimenters, disposing their high-pressure and low-pressure cylinders differently, and using rather more common sense, managed better than he did. One in particular, Thomas W. Worsdell, who had at one time assisted Webb at Crewe and who had been promoted from there to the position of Locomotive Superintendent on the Great Eastern Railway, built quite a number of compounds, beginning while he was in charge at Stratford on the Great Eastern and continuing when he went on to Gateshead on the North Eastern. The type of compounding he chose could not be deemed unsuccessful, though his successor modified many of the engines he constructed, converting them to single expansion locomotives. He found his inspiration in Germany, in a 2-4-0 compound introduced on the Hanover State Railway during the earlier 'eighties of the nineteenth century.

Herr von Borries, that railway's Mechanical Engineer, built some two-cylinder 2-4-0s for fast passenger work, each of which had a high-pressure cylinder on the right-hand side and a low-pressure one on the left, both outside the frames, with an intermediate steam receiver linking them. It was by British standards a most ungainly machine, with an enormous steam dome almost as high as the width of the boiler, another dome containing sand for the wheels which sheltered behind the larger one, a safety valve that looked like a tuning fork which had been inserted into the top of the firebox, a stovepipe chimney resembling the business end of a blunderbuss and a huge steam pipe which emerged from the steam dome and led down to the smaller high-pressure cylinder. It was no thing of beauty, but it appears to have fulfilled its designer's expectations, and it gave Worsdell the stimulus to design much more shapely engines which bore little external indication that they were compounds at all.

One hindrance which Herr von Borries had to overcome was that, while a two-cylinder simple locomotive with its cranks set at right angles was always in a position to start, if a two-cylinder compound were to

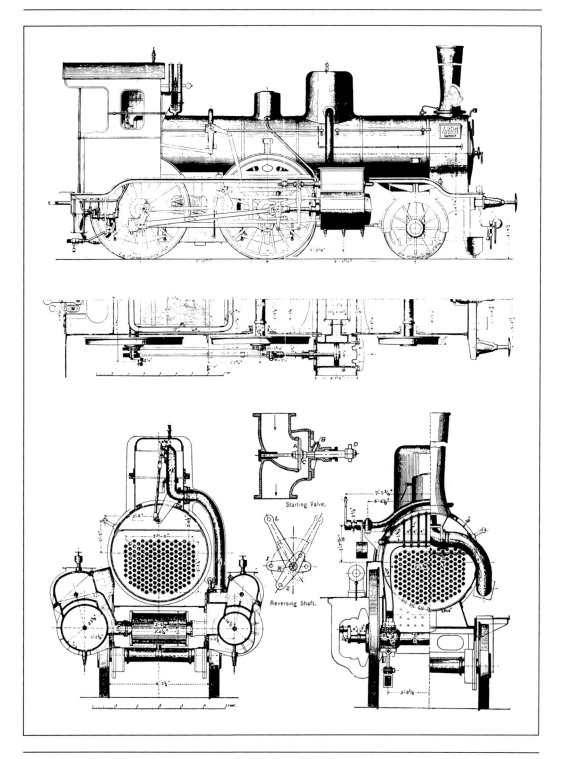

Starting Valve.

Reversing Shaft.

come to a halt with the high-pressure piston at the very end of its stroke, forwards or rearwards, no pressure could then be exerted effectively on the crank to which it was connected, the force of any steam entering the cylinder being directed along the line of the crank itself. Further, the low-pressure cylinder cannot assist the other because the latter is not giving it any steam. Von Borries circumvented this difficulty by fixing a special valve on a spindle in the pipe between the receiver and the low-pressure cylinder, so that steam could enter the latter direct from the boiler and press against the piston. Once the wheels had turned round a few times, and the receiver was full of steam exhausted from the high-pressure cylinder, the pressure of that steam closed the valve and full compounding began.

In adapting von Borries' method for the locomotives he himself designed, Worsdell made a number of changes. In the first place, following, the now usual British custom, he set both cylinders between the frames, under the smokebox, to work on interior cranks. Secondly he modified the special steam admission valve at the entry to the low-pressure cylinder by making it a simple flap-valve which was closed and held back in position by the pressure in the receiver as soon as this was built up sufficiently. This was a less complicated device than von Borries' spindle valve, and it worked just as well when the high-presssure piston would not start the locomotive. Thirdly, instead of the intermediate receiver being a box adjacent to the cylinders, it took the form of a pipe 6 inches wide which looped upwards, across and downwards within the smokebox in much the same manner as in Webb's compounds. Fourthly, he employed Joy's valve gear, not Walschaerts', as von Borries had done. There being no room between the cylinders for steam admission valves, he placed them above.

The first locomotives built to this design emerged from Stratford works in 1884, and were followed by others. Worsdell had already built 20 simple-expansion 2–4–0s which were like the compounds in all respects save in not being compounds, in having a lower boiler pressure (140 instead of 160 lbs per square inch) and in having two front carrying wheels instead of a four-wheeled bogie. The coupled wheels in both classes were 7 feet in diameter. The two types were tested against one another. It was then found that the automatic flap valve caused problems. In the words of E.L. Ahrons (*The British Steam Railway Locomotive, 1825–1925*, Chapter 18):

'When the engine was new the starting arrangement consisted simply of a valve whereby boiler steam could be admitted to the low-pressure cylinder, but this steam immediately travelled round to the exhaust side of the high-pressure cylinder and blocked the piston, so that about once in ten times the engine failed to start. To obviate this an intercepting flap valve worked from the footplate was placed in the receiver pipe and was closed by the driver before the starting valve was opened. As the engine moved, the first exhaust from the high-pressure cylinder automatically opened the valve and allowed this steam to pass directly to the low-pressure cylinder. This arrangement differed in detail, though it was similar in principle, from that subsequently used on the North Eastern Railway.'

At first it appeared that these locomotives were more economical in working than the 20 non-compound ones against which they were tested. However, the latter's boilers were only pressed to 140 lbs per square inch, whereas the compounds had 160 lbs, and the 14 per cent saving in fuel consumption observed in the first tests dropped to only two per cent when the compounds' 160 lbs was reduced to 150 lbs. So, if pressure in the simple-expansion engines had been raised to that figure it might well have been that they would have proved equally economical — or even slightly better. Furthermore, the compounds do not seem to have been all that successful as motive power units. They pulled well at low speeds, but when required to run fast did not readily respond.

Soon after these engines had been built, T.W. Worsdell moved to the North Eastern, and in 1885 at Gateshead he completed a compound express goods engine, an 0–6–0, with two cylinders of the same sizes as those on the Stratford-built engines and similarly arranged, with the same type of valve gear and the same boiler pressure. He also began the tradition, continued until the end of the North Eastern's separate existence, of providing commodious cabs for the engine crews. In his monograph on *North Eastern Locomotives*, O.S. Nock comments appreciatively on these cabs' handsome interior finish, lined with painted and polished wood. Worsdell built many others of this type, and after he had retired from his Superintendency his successor built many more, until 170 in all had been produced. They had a reputation for being light on coal, and they tackled without difficulty the fast through freight trains which plied along the main line between Newcastle and Leeds, as well as those on the Newcastle-Carlisle line and the few that were routed across the Pennines between Darlington and Tebay over the severe gradients of the Stainmore route.

Next after the construction of the first 0–6–0s came a number of 0–6–2 tank engines, 51 being built as compounds and 11 as non-compounds. The former were basically the same as the 0–6–0s except in having tanks and a coal bunker instead of a tender. They were intended for short-haul goods trains such as those which worked between Tyneside and Consett ironworks along a line of extremely fierce gradients, and by all accounts acquitted themselves creditably.

Worsdell now turned his attention to passenger train haulage. At the end of 1886 he completed a 2–4–0 compound, in which he raised the boiler pressure to 170 lbs per square inch and modified the Joy's valve gear so that the low-pressure cylinder always had a later cut-off than the

Right *A cross-sectional view of one of T.W. Worsdell's 0-6-2 tank locomotives. The path of the steam from the high-pressure to the low-pressure cylinder can be traced, going round the interior of the smokebox in a wide pipe marked in dotted lines. (The Engineer)*

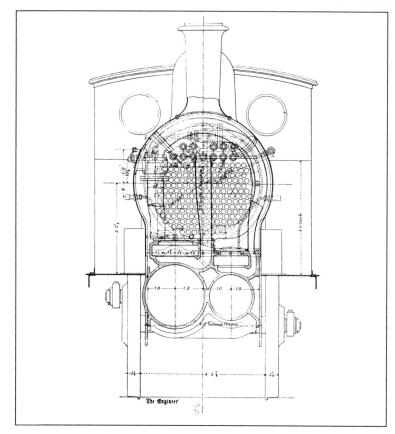

Below *Contemporary engraving of one of T.W. Worsdell's two cylinder compound freight engines, which bears no external signs of being a compound at all. (The Engineer)*

No 1324, T.W. Worsdell's first two-cylinder compound passenger locomotive design. As with his freight engine, there is nothing to give away the fact of its being a compound. (NRM)

high-pressure cylinder; this was done to secure approximately the same work from each. The alternative would have been to increase the diameter of the low-pressure cylinder, but there was not sufficient room between the frames for this if the cylinders were to be set beside each other, so the proportion between their diameters needed to be less than the calculated 2.3:1 which von Borries had believed to be the ideal figure. The coupled wheels were 6 ft 8 in across and the boiler and firebox had a heating surface of over 1,300 sq ft, 16 per cent greater than in the goods engines.

When tested, this locomotive proved to be a very powerful puller, but at high speeds it was unsteady and had a loud raucous exhaust. Worsdell nevertheless considered it to be a success, and after it had spent three months on main-line duties he withdrew it for display in the Newcastle Jubilee Exhibition of 1887. At the same time he built another with the same wheel arrangement, but using piston valves instead of slide valves. A fault of the latter type of valve was that if the engine 'primed' (ie if water came over from the boiler into the cylinders along with the steam) they were liable to suffer damage. Worsdell's Chief Draughtsman, Walter M. Smith, a brilliant engineer whose career was cut short by an early death, had devised a piston valve which had two small spring-loaded exit valves in its casing, one at each end of the barrel, through which priming water could escape before it did any harm. (It turned out to be not entirely successful, since inexperienced enginemen did not open the valves soon enough and damage ensured).

With further locomotives of this class Worsdell substituted a front bogie for the leading carrying wheels. Ten were built as simple-expansion and ten as compound engines. Like the 2–4–0s that preceded them, the compounds were very free running. In the 'Race to Edinburgh' during the summer of 1888, one of them, No 117, made a record time of 126 minutes non-stop from Newcastle to Edinburgh with a load of 100 tons, the distance being 124.4 miles.

In the same year Worsdell surprised everybody by building a batch of single-driver compounds. The construction of single driving express

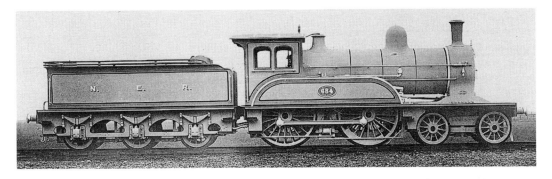

No 684, T.W. Worsdell's further development of the 2-4-0 two-cylinder compound shown in the previous illustration. The only difference between the two was that the second had a leading bogie instead of a two-wheeled truck, which made for steadier running. (NRM)

passenger engines had begun again, after an intermission of many years, for reasons indicated below in Chapter 9. Only on the Great Northern Railway had their construction never been discontinued. Ten were built at Gateshead with 7 ft diameter driving wheels to be used on the fast trains between Leeds and Scarborough. They had the same cylinder sizes and arrangements as their 0-6-0, 2-4-0 and 4-4-0 predecessors, but differed from them in one respect. If one examined the right-hand side of the engine one could see the wall of the low-pressure cylinder bulging through a hole in the side of the frame. Charles Rous-Marten, writing in the July 1902 issue of *The Railway Magazine*, described a run he had had behind No 1330, the first to be built:

'I had No 1330 on the Leeds-Scarborough Special, the fast express which leaves Leeds every evening at 5.5 and runs to Scarborough, 67¾ miles, passing through York without halting. The load was the usual light one, of 5 bogie coaches, weighing in all 126 tons .... No 1330 made a very fine run, doing the journey from Leeds to Scarborough, start to stop, in 72 minutes 14 seconds inclusive, with a bad relaying slack at Waterloo junction and a worse signal check at Huttons Ambo, the latter very nearly a stop. The net time to Scarborough was only 69¾ minutes, making no allowance for the regular service slacks at Church Fenton junction, at York station and round the Kirkham curves. This was one of the best runs I have had with that splendid train. A speed of 80.3 miles an hour was attained down the Micklefield bank, and the final stage of 42 miles from York (passing) to Scarborough (stop) was covered in 41 minutes 44 seconds net. The last 21 miles from Malton to the Scarborough stop occupied 20 minutes 40 seconds. All the prescribed service slacks were most strictly observed.'

After constructing the seven-footers Worsdell also built ten compound single-drivers with 7 ft 6 in driving wheels and somewhat larger cylinders. The increased sizes of the latter obliged him to adopt an unusual expedient in order to accommodate them within the frames. With the earlier machines he had, as we have seen, to allow the low-pressure cylinder to bulge out through the framing. With the later ones he used a different tactic. Instead of trying to set the two cylinders exactly side by side he positioned the high-pressure cylinder a little below the level of the driving wheel axle with the piston rod inclined slightly upwards. The other cylinder, on the other hand, had its axis slightly above the axle-level and was inclined slightly downwards. This allowed him to bring the left-hand side of the larger cylinder above the right-hand side of the smaller one. A further consequence of using such large cylinders was that the valve chests could not be placed anywhere else than laterally outwards from them, so that they were visible on either side under the running plate. They were operated by Joy's valve gear, set within the frames and working through rocking bars. These engines had the same total heating surface as the seven-footers, but a larger grate area.

Below left *No 779, one of T.W. Worsdell's 4-4-0 compound express engines, waiting to back on to a train. The North Eastern livery used at the time for express passenger engines — light green with dark green borders — shows up well. (NRM)*

Below *No 1517, one of T.W. Worsdell's second batch of 4-2-2 two-cylinder compounds with 7 ft 6 in driving wheels. Astonishingly, they were intended to supersede existing 4-4-0s on heavy East Coast expresses between York and Edinburgh. This particular locomotive hauled a load of 270 tons between Newcastle and Berwick-on-Tweed, 66.9 miles, in 78 minutes. On another occasion, with a load a little over half as heavy, it reached a speed of 90 mph. (NRM)*

A cross-sectional diagram of No 1517, showing the enormous size of the low-pressure cylinder and the situation of the valve chests outside the frames, where alone there was room to position them. In the previous illustration their covers can be seen behind the smokebox wing plates.
(The Engineer)

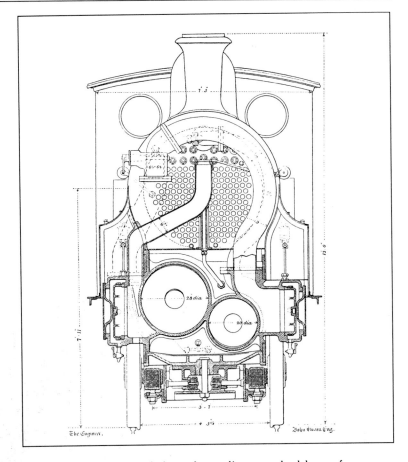

They were not intended, as the earlier ones had been, for use on secondary main-line services with fairly light loads, but for use with fast main-line expresses, and were provided with suitably large tenders which each held nearly 4,000 gallons of water. Behind their introduction lay the expectation that loads would increase and schedules be tightened once the Forth Bridge had been completed and through running to Aberdeen by the East Coast route became possible. The first of the new locomotives to be built, on being put to the test, hauled a train of 270 tons between Newcastle and Berwick-on-Tweed, 66.9 miles, in 78 minutes. On another occasion, with the same locomotive and a load a little over half that weight, travelling between the same two places, 90 miles an hour was attained at one point — a most unusual maximum speed for the time. The second engine of this batch showed during indicator trials that it could put out well in excess of 1,000 horse power at high speed.The same trials also made it clear that both high-pressure and low-pressure cylinders were doing approximately equal work — something that, among Webb's three-cylinder compounds, only the 'Teutonics' came near achieving.

Such being their proved ability, the fact that they were soon rebuilt as non-compounds requires some explanation. The fact was that their valve gear constantly needed repairing. This was partly due to its complications, especially in the system of rocking levers. As soon as T.W. Worsdell left Gateshead (ill-health obliging him to retire early), his younger brother and successor, Wilson Worsdell, rebuilt all the 7 ft 6 in singles as non-compounds, and substituted Stephenson's valve gear for Joy's. The change in no way affected their performance but increased their availability.

Was the Worsdell-von Borries system a success? A qualified one, it would seem. It is perhaps significant that von Borries himself went over to four-cylinder compounding on the Hanover State Railway. Charles Rous-Marten, who was a great admirer of the French four-cylinder compound system, did not consider the two-cylinder system altogether a success, though, as seen above, he could praise the performance of an individual locomotive. He believed that with the two-cylinder system, equilibrium between the cylinders was next to impossible to achieve. So it was not long before the seven-foot singles were also converted into non-compounds, as also were the 12 four-coupled engines. With the compound goods locomotives and goods tank locomotives it was otherwise. Wilson Worsdell continued to turn them out to his brother's design until 1892. He had no prejudice against compounding. When he built his first two 'M' Class 4-4-0s, which were to achieve such distinction in the 1895 'Race to Aberdeen', he built one compound 4-4-0 on his brother's principle to match them, giving it a boiler pressure of 200 lbs per square inch. However, its performance did not surpass those of its non-compound sisters, and it was not used on any of the racing trains in 1895.

At the turn of the century, British locomotive practice was still therefore not in favour of compounding, though two-cylinder, three cylinder and four-cylinder arrangements had been tried — including the rather unusual method described in the next chapter. Other experiments were about to follow, and on one line, the Midland, the three-cylinder arrangement proved so successful that several hundreds of the 'Crimson Ramblers', as the 4-4-0 Midland compounds came to be termed (for they were found on all parts of the far-extending London, Midland & Scottish system) were built, mostly after the 1923 groupings. It could certainly be said that both Webb and T.W. Worsdell gave their different systems a fair trial. With goods locomotives, where what was required was the ability to pull hard at low speeds, Worsdell's system showed itself as good as simple action. But it was not so markedly better in terms of performance and coal-saving that its advantages outweighed the disadvantages of extra complications, so it did not long outlast its chief protagonist.

8

Four-cylinder tandem compounds

While Webb's and Worsdell's compound locomotives were being designed and constructed on the London & North Western Railway and the North Eastern Railway, two other lines were experimenting with a third system. In this each of the two driving cranks was operated by both a high-pressure and a low-pressure cylinder, the two working with a common piston rod. This 'tandem' method, patented by W.H. Nesbit in 1884, had the advantage of allowing all four cylinders to be accommodated within the engine framing. It also greatly lessened the number of rotating and reciprocating parts.

The first locomotive to be produced in Britain on Nesbit's principle was actually a rebuild of an earlier simple-acting engine, a 4–4–0 designed and built by Thomas Wheatley in 1871 when he was Locomotive Superintendent of the North British Railway. No 224 was notorious in having become one of the victims of the most dramatic railway tragedy of the nineteenth century, when in January 1879 the central girders of the first Tay Bridge were blown down in a violent storm while a train was actually passing across them, carrying driver, fireman, guard and 75 passengers to a watery grave. The engine, however, was eventually recovered from the bed of the estuary and discovered not to be an absolute wreck. It was towed back to Glasgow on its own wheels, minus cab, chimney and dome, and was stored in the North British Company's works at Cowlairs, until Dugald Drummond, Wheatley's successor, rebuilt it without much changing its appearance. (Damage to it had been relatively slight since it had been encased within a span of girders when it fell into the water, and these had acted as shock absorbers). Drummond eventually departed to take up a similar position at St Rollox works on the Caledonian Railway, and Matthew Holmes succeeded him. The latter decided to use No 224 for an experimental trial of Nesbit's system.

After its second rebuilding its appearance was much altered; it now *looked* as if Drummond had rebuilt it, whereas before it had not. In regard to the compounding arrangements, the smaller high-pressure cylinders were placed right in the front, well ahead of the smokebox and just behind the buffer-beam. The steam pipes leading to them projected forwards from the regulator under the dome, then downwards through the smokebox, then forwards and downwards again beneath a casing below the smokebox front, and finally forwards once more to reach their destination. From each high-pressure cylinder a single long piston rod continued backwards to pass through both ends of the low pressure cylinder and its piston before reaching the little end of the connecting rod, which drove on the front axle of the coupled wheels. A modified version of Joy's valve gear, operating from the connecting rod, controlled the slide valves above both cylinders. Both valves could be separately adjusted to give different cut-offs if desired. Steam from both high-pressure cylinders passed to the low pressure ones by means of a wide, centrally-sited pipe; there was no intermediate steam receiver. In this way steam exhausted from the front cylinders was used almost at once in the rear ones, with little loss of heat *en route*. The ratio between the volumes of the high-pressure and low-pressure cylinders was 1:2.36. The accompanying diagram shows all these arrangements fairly clearly.

No 224 ran as a compound until 1897, when it was rebuilt for the third time, as a two-cylinder simple-acting engine. It was scrapped in 1919. No details were ever published about its performance as a compound. It worked for some years on trains between Edinburgh and Glasgow, but for a long while no driver would consent to take it across the second Tay Bridge as it was deemed an unlucky engine and was known as 'The

A detailed sectional diagram of the North British Railway's 4-4-0 No 224 (the locomotive which had been involved in the Tay Bridge accident of January 1879) as rebuilt by M. Holmes on Nesbit's patent compound system, with high-pressure and low-pressure cylinders in tandem. (The Engineer)

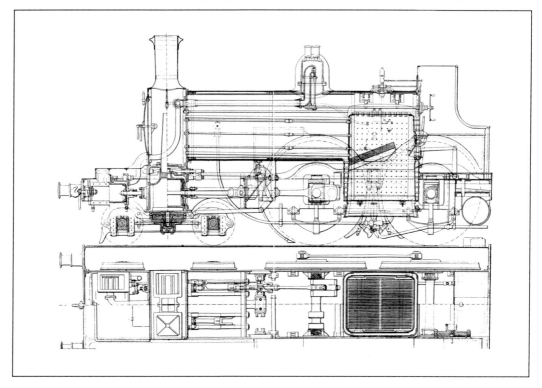

W. Dean's experimental 2-4-0 compound locomotive, built on the Nesbit principle with high-pressure and low-pressure cylinders in tandem side by side within the frames, in 1886. (NRM)

Diver'. However it suffered no further mishaps. Evidently there was not enough improvement, if any, in quality of performance or fuel economy over similarly-sized non-compounds to warrant Nesbit's method being perpetuated. It was the only compound locomotive to be produced in Scotland.

The other locomotive engineer to try the tandem system was William Dean on the Great Western Railway, who built two such engines in 1886, one for the standard and one for the broad gauge. Both were 2–4–0s, and in neither was there anything in their external appearance to betray to the casual eye that they were not two cylinder locomotives of conventional pattern. No 7, the standard gauge locomotive, was double-framed, had driving wheels 7 feet in diameter and 4-foot leading wheels placed well forward to allow room for the cylinders and valves, and having some side-play in the axlebox horns. All six wheels had exterior springing. The total effect was neat and workmanlike.

In regard to the compounding arrangements, unlike those in the North British engine the low-pressure cylinders were ahead of the high-pressure ones, immediately beneath the smokebox and above the front carrying wheels. On either side, each pair of cylinders was in one casting. A hollow tubular cover separated the one from the other; it was fastened by studs and nuts to the larger forward cylinder and fitted into the front of the smaller rear one. Within it was a bush about 6 inches long, through which the common piston rod slid to and fro, the latter being 4 inches wide in the front cylinder but half an inch narrower in the rear one. On each side Stephenson's valve gear operated a rod attached to the middle of a half-moon-shaped yoke jointed at either end to the valve spindles for the two cylinders, so that both valve events were the same in either cylinder at the same moment. An unusual feature was that the cut-offs were arranged to be different in forward stroke and back stroke — 69.7 per cent and 53.2 per cent in full gear, 27.1 per cent and 19 per cent on the first notch of the lever. The driver could admit boiler steam, albeit at reduced pressure, to the low-pressure cylinders when he thought it necessary, and a relief valve was placed in the steam chest.

E.L. Ahrons, who describes this engine and its broad gauge fellow in his book *The British Steam Railway Locomotive, 1825–1925,* was personally involved with both locomotives during their trials, and discussed them with Dean, who told him that he conceived it to be his duty to experiment with compounding, and that the tandem arrangement seemed the obvious one to try since Webb's and Worsdell's systems were receiving extensive trials elsewhere. He had expected difficulties to arise in practice, and they certainly did. On No 7 it was the bushes on the piston rods which gave trouble. It proved impossible to lubricate them properly, so that the rods became badly scratched longitudinally. The cylinders would have been better if further apart, as they were in the North British engine, but this would have necessitated extending the whole front end of the locomotive and giving it a leading bogie, and would also have increased the weight of the reciprocating parts. The engine ran for some while between Swindon and Cardiff by way of Gloucester, but was never put in charge of express trains.

No 8 the broad gauge engine, resembled No 7 in side view, except that the driving wheels had inside framing and springs, a splasher for the coupling rod outside those for the driving wheels on either side, and a

Dean's other four-cylinder tandem compound built for use on the broad gauge. Had it not been scrapped after an accident it would have been rebuilt to match its narrow gauge fellow. (Bracken Books)

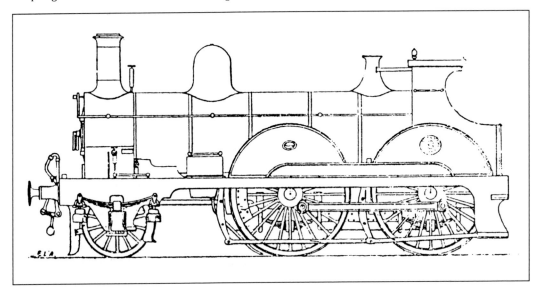

straight running plate from front to back. Between the frames, however, there were considerable differences from No 7's arrangements, since it was a broad gauge engine and there was more room for manoeuvre. As with its fellow, the low-pressure cylinders were ahead of the high-pressure ones, but the dimensions were different. Also, the cylinders were not horizontal, but inclined slightly downwards towards the crank axle. The steam chests were beneath them, and the valves were directly driven by Stephenson's gear. The really unusual feature was the piston rod arrangement. E.L. Ahrons, in the book mentioned above, describes it:

'The low-pressure pistons each had two rods, which issued from stuffing-boxes outside and at the sides of the small high-pressure cylinders. The end partition between the high-pressure and low-pressure cylinders was in one piece with the main casting, since no bush was required; in fact, all four cylinders were cast in one piece. The high-pressure piston rod was central. There were two slide bars, and the crosshead had projecting wings on either side, to which the two outer low-pressure piston rods were secured by nuts, the central high-pressure rod being connected to the crosshead in the usual manner. Each other rod was 9 in from the central rod, centre to centre'.

No 8 should really have been No 13; it was unlucky from the start and had several bad accidents during its trials. The final one, after which it was never used again, happened dramatically inside Box tunnel when, piloted by another broad gauge 2–4–0, *Acheron*, it headed an up express between Bristol and Swindon. The driver of the pilot engine, a Welshman from Cardiff, was instructed merely to give his own engine enough steam to move itself; No 8 was to do the pulling. (Presumably the reason for the piloting was a suspicion that something might go wrong). While the train was actually traversing Box tunnel, going up a 1 in 100 incline, catastrophe occurred. Three of the four pistons in the compound suddenly disintegrated. There was a tremendous explosion, steam went everywhere and fragments of the smashed pistons were shot out of the chimney to rebound from the roof of the tunnel and bounce back to shower the footplate with shrapnel. Fortunately no one on the footplate took any harm. Meanwhile, the driver of *Acheron*, realizing that they had to get out of the tunnel as quickly as possible, gave his engine all the steam he could, and eventually the train emerged, no one having suffered any damage except to their nerves, though everyone on both footplates had had the shock of their lives. No 8 was taken off, hauled to Swindon and there dismantled. If it had performed satisfactorily it would eventually have been rebuilt to correspond with No 7 once the broad gauge had been abolished. Had this happened, the peculiar piston rod arrangement would have been discarded as there would then have been no room for it.

The tandem system was not tried out on any other British railway, no doubt partly because of the unfortunate mishaps that beset Dean's engines. At first sight it would seem that the troubles experienced by No 7 might have been eliminated by suitable modifications. On the face of it, this compounding system seems neater than a three-cylinder or four-cylinder method in which each piston drives a separate crank. However, one fault was unavoidable — the fore-and-aft thrusts of heavy reciprocating masses. Unbalance in rotary movement can be largely corrected by appropriately weighting the insides of driving wheel rims, but there is no way of correcting reciprocating imbalance. The consequence was an uncomfortable surging backwards and forwards in the train itself, like that occasionally felt by those who travelled behind Webb's three-cylinder compounds. Whatever economies might be effected by locomotives constructed on the tandum principle, the end would be defeated if people refused to travel behind them because of the discomfort they caused. So it is to be presumed that Mr Nesbit's patent did not bring him in much money.

9

Drummond's double-singles

Dugald Drummond, one of the great locomotive engineers of pre-grouping railway history and, like so many others of his kind, a Scot by birth, combined cleverness, cunning and caution with a flair for success. He learned his trade at Brighton under Stroudley, and then went as Locomotive Superintendent first to the North British Railway, to provide it with a stud of 4-4-0s which could keep time on through expresses to and from England over the fearsome gradients of the newly opened Waverley route, and afterwards to the Caledonian, where he reorganized the locomotive stock to the great satisfaction of the Board, setting a pattern for express engines which, with modifications, was to last until the 1923 groupings. Finally, after a brief foray into Australia, where he hoped to make his fortune as a partner in a locomotive manufacturing business but found the prospects much less bright when he actually arrived there, he applied for the post of Locomotive Superintendent on the London & South Western Railway, William Adams being on the point of retirement, and went to Nine Elms in 1895. During the period of his superintendency there, which he held until his death, he designed some highly successful 4-4-0 express engines of characteristic appearance, some rather less successful 4-6-0s and a peculiar group of half a dozen locomotives, the 'double singles', with which this chapter is concerned.

He was a forceful character who could take strong likes and dislikes; he venerated his old chief, Stroudley, and for some reason loathed S.W. Johnson of the Midland, whose colleague he had been at Brighton. Like the outer frieze of the Parthenon, his personality was sculptured in high relief and matched the vigour of its contending Centaurs and Lapiths. His command of Clydeside invective was total: not for him the finer nuances of delicate irony. His reproofs to footplate staff who mismanaged their engines could be scalding; it was perhaps fitting, if unfortunate, that he should meet his end by being accidentally scalded by steam from one of his own engines.

The later years of the nineteenth century saw a brief revival of single-driving engines of the 4-2-2 wheel arrangement. The express locomotives of the past had for a long while been single drivers, and they still reigned supreme on the Great Northern, as also on the Great Western until the end of the broad gauge in 1892. Other lines, however, increasingly had resource to coupled driving wheels in order to obtain better adhesion. If loads could have been kept down to, say, under 200 tons, and average speeds to not much more than 50 miles an hour, there would have been much to be said for the single-driver. The provision of tractive effort in a steam locomotive has nothing to do with the number of coupled wheels but varies directly with the cylinder capacity and boiler pressure, and inversely with the diameter of the driving wheels. So long as a single driver could do its work without slipping, it had the great advantage of simplicity in construction and relative fewness of moving parts, and there was more room for the firegrate when there was no rear coupled axle to get in its way. However, slipping *was* a problem, both when a train was being started and when it was being taken up a severe gradient. Skilful driving techniques could to some extent counter this tendency. An expert engineman knew to a nicety how much to open out his engine on starting without reaching the point when the wheels ceased to grip the rails. Continuous and imperceptible slipping at speed, however, could not be easily avoided.

On many main lines there were long and severe banks, and coupled wheels were necessary to ensure adequate adhesion. In theory one could obtain the latter by piling weight on a single pair of driving wheels, but beyond a certain point the track would not endure it. The point varied from one railway company to another, and the men who knew what it was, the Civil Engineer and his assistants, could veto the use of any engine which they regarded as too heavy. So coupling was forced on most locomotive engineers who found, perhaps to their surprise, that it made no difference to freedom of running. The London & North Western Railway obtained much higher maximum speeds from their 2-4-0 'Precedents' than from the singles whose places they took. On many lines, especially north of the Scottish border, the single driver almost vanished from the scene. Then something happened which appeared to offer it a new lease of life.

Mr Holt, the Works Manager at Derby on the Midland Railway, devised a method of sanding which worked from compressed air supplied by the Westinghouse brake reservoir, and this was tested out on the gradients of the Settle and Carlisle line using a 2-4-0 locomotive which had had its coupling rods removed so that it was in effect a 2-2-2. Sand was not simply dropped in front of the wheels, but was blown under them. However, the Westinghouse Brake Company objected that this was an improper use of compressed air which was needed to operate the train's brakes. So steam pressure was substituted and proved just as effective. It was found that even single driving wheels could keep a grip on the 1 in 100 gradients with the assistance of such sanding. The question then posed itself — why couple wheels at all when the loads to be moved were not excessive (which, on the Midland, with passenger trains, they never were?) The company took the hint, and during the last decade of the nineteenth century S.W. Johnson built nearly a hundred 4-2-2s for use south of Leeds. Some other main-line companies followed suit. James Holden on the Great Eastern, H. Pollitt on the Great Central and (as already noticed) T.W. Worsdell on the North Eastern also built a few. A single driver, the famous No 123 which showed its paces during the 1888 'Race to Edinburgh', was also purchased by the Caledonian. (It bore every appearance of having been designed by Drummond, but the latter never claimed responsibility for it; it appears to have been built by Neilson and Co as a show engine for the Edinburgh International Exhibition of 1886, and the Caledonian bought it subsequently). On the Great Northern, Patrick Stirling had never stopped producing his celebrated eight-footers until he died in harness in 1895; his successor, H.A. Ivatt, who was to astonish everyone later with his huge 'Atlantics', built a dozen singles of his own design to supplement Stirling's, some of which later he also modified by giving them domes. On the Great Western, Dean, at the time of the change-over from broad to narrow gauge, rebuilt a number of existing 2-2-2s as 4-2-2s. The single-driver seemed set to enjoy a new lease of life, though in the end it proved to be only a St Martin's summer.

On the London & South Western Railway, the Board of Directors had been leaning rather heavily on William Adams to build some single-wheelers, and designs for such a locomotive had been duly prepared. When Drummond succeeded Adams in 1895 he acknowledged the pressure in an unexpected way. He knew well enough that a 4-2-2 single, however relatively cheap it might be to build and maintain, was not the sort of engine to cope with the South Western's steepest gradients, which, on the main line to Southampton and Salisbury, were lengthy though moderate, and which west of Salisbury were in places as bad as the approaches to Shap and Beattock from the south — especially between Exeter and Plymouth. He saw no reason why he should build yesterday's engines to pull tomorrow's loads. So he laid before the Board a proposal to incorporate, in effect, two single-driving mechanisms in one frame under one boiler. This was a doubly unique conception. No locomotive had yet been built in this country which had a leading bogie and two uncoupled driving axles, nor any with four driving wheels, coupled or uncoupled, with four cylinders, all simple-expansion (though J. Manson was about to introduce a four-cylinder 4-4-0 on the Glasgow & South Western).

Gaining permission to proceed, Drummond set about building the new engine, having in mind other innovations as well as the 'double-single' principle. One was a long firebox. He did what he would not have ventured to do if he had coupled the driving wheels, and set the centres of the latter as much as 11 feet apart, thus having plenty of room for the firegrate behind the cranks on the front axle, which were operated by the inside cylinders. The outside cylinders were set well along the frame to the rear of the leading bogie and operated on the rear axle. Separate and different valve gears worked both pairs of cylinders, Stephenson's

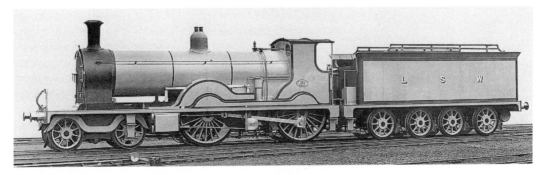

inside and Joy's outside, and both were power-operated from the cab.

In order to increase the ability of the boiler to produce steam Drummond introduced a device list used in some locomotives on the Birmingham & Derby Railway during 1841–2 — cross water tubes in the firebox. Since the water-tube principle was later to be exploited, though in a different manner, by two other chief mechanical engineers, something ougth to be said about it here in its Drummond version.

The classical steam locomotive boiler, as first designed by Stephenson and continuing unaltered in principle throughout the nineteenth century, received heat for its contents partly through the walls of the firebox and partly through a large number of firetubes which, covered by the water in the boiler, extended forwards from the front of the firebox to the back of the smokebox. Hot gases of combustion were sucked through them by the partial vacuum created in the smokebox through the blast from the cylinders. However, the transference of heat to the water through the tube walls was never complete. There was not enough time during the passage of the gases between firebox and smokebox — a mere matter of seconds — to allow more than a portion of the heat to be given up; the rest passed out through the exhaust and was wasted. Most steam was in fact produced where the boiler was in direct contact with the firebox, whose inner sides, exposed to the radiant heat from the burning coal, were very hot indeed.

Dugald Drummond's first 'double single', No 720, as originally built and painted in Stroudley's dark ochre livery. The absence of water-troughs on the LSWR system was the reason for the large eight-wheeled tender. (NRM)

A dimensional diagram of Drummond's first 'double single'. (Ian Allan)

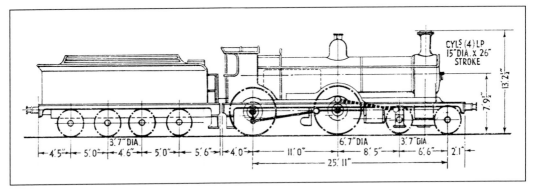

Could the amount of firebox contact be increased? Drummond's method of doing so was to insert tubes laterally across the furnace area above the level of the firebox door; they sloped slightly upwards from one side to the other, and contained water continuous with that in the main boiler. Here the most intense heat would be experienced and the most rapid boiling would take place; bubbles of steam would emerge from the upper end of each tube to join the rest of the vapour in the upper part of the boiler, while hot water from the lower part of the boiler would flow in to take its place.

So long as the tubes were strong enough to withstand the pressure, and the metal of which they were made was able to withstand the heat of the furnace without deteriorating, this method promised to increase the heating surface considerably without taking up too much room or greatly increasing the engine's weight. The tubes would, of course, need cleaning out just as the boiler did, when the locomotive was withdrawn for maintenance. In the first double-single, as first constructed, it was necessary to remove the outer cladding from the firebox sides to do this, but as we shall see Drummond soon reconstructed the engine by placing a removable rectangular casing on either side, somewhat higher on the right than on the left to correspond with the slope of the tubes; this when removed gave easy access to the tubes. These casings became a recognizable feature of nearly all the express engines he subsequently built.

The cylinders of the new locomotive were 15 in by 26 in, the inside ones being part of a single casting, while the outer ones were bolted to

The official diagram showing the speeds achieved in relation to gradients by No 720 when officially tested with 300 tons on 19 May 1898 (the chart reads from right to left).
(The Engineer)

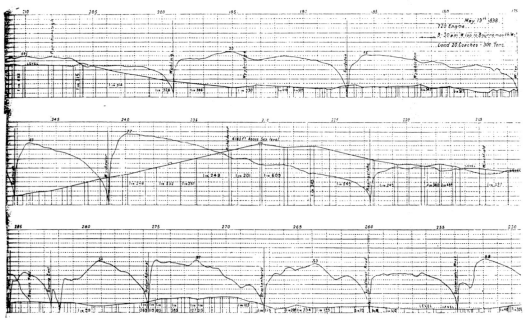

the frames. An anomalous feature of the design was the provision of coupling rod splashers outside the driving wheel splashers, though there were no coupling rods for them to accommodate. To complete the tally of innovations, an organ pipe whistle replaced the usual highly pitched type.

If native cunning was shown in some of the unusual features, native caution displayed itself in the building of a single prototype, to be thoroughly tested before more were constructed. When the engine first emerged from Nine Elms works it caused quite a stir. For some reason, perhaps so that it could be more readily distinguished at a distance, perhaps as a tribute to the memory of his former chief, Drummond had it painted in Stroudley's livery of golden ochre, offset with dark green and crimson lake. With a very large tender carried on eight wheels with inside springing — the type later irreverently designated as 'the Drummond water-cart' — No 720 was easily the largest express locomotive ever put on London & South Western metals. It remained to be seen whether it measured up to its job.

It was run in on slow trains and then given an official test in May 1898. *The Engineer* reported favourably on it:

'This is a magnificent engine, and when we remember that it has a tractive effort of 16,290 lb we need not be susrprised to learn that it can keep time easily with no less than 22 double-bogie coaches.'

One does not have, of course, to think in terms of bogie carriages weighing 30 tons or so each, such as were built in later years. No platform at Waterloo would have been able to accommodate such a train, and probably no four-coupled locomotive then in existence in this country could even have started it from rest. On the test run the load is given as 300 tons, and the train's timing was an easy one, with stops to be made at Surbiton, Woking, Basingstoke, Winchester, Eastleigh, Southampton West, Lyndhurst Road, Brockenhurst, Hinton Admiral, Bournemouth East, Bournemouth Central and Bournemouth West. A maximum of 46 was reached before Surbiton, 50 before Woking, and 44½ beyond Farnborough; 35 was the minimum at the top of the ascent to Litchfield tunnel, 77 was attained before shutting off steam for Winchester and 67 again before Eastleigh. After that no speed higher than 57 was attained on the undulating road between Southampton and Bournemouth. Only nine miles were covered at more than the mile-a-minute rate during the whole journey. The record of this run, as published in *The Engineer*, does not give start-to-stop timings on the separate stages, but time was evidently kept with, for the period, an unusually high maximum speed near Winchester. On another occasion 79 miles an hour was reached down a 1 in 70 incline, when the cut-off was 17 per cent and the boiler pressure 165 lbs per square inch. Where this happened is not stated — perhaps descending eastward from Honiton tunnel.

In its issue of 7 October 1897 *The Engineer* reported that No 720 was 'quite realising all that Mr Drummond anticipated, and appears to provide a most satisfactory solution of the heavy fast-train problem'. Such an estimate was altogether too optimistic. The locomotive men did not take to the new engine at all, and Drummond found it necessary to call a meeting of senior drivers in order to explain the thinking behind the design. The men listened politely but were not won over. The facts were that only with great difficulty could the engine be persuaded to start a heavy train, and once it had started it did not steam properly. A long series of tests took place between Clapham Junction and Eastleigh before the locomotive was released for general service in November 1898. It was then put on Bournemouth expresses but showed no improvement in performance over the Adams outside-cylindered 4-4-0s which had hitherto operated these trains, and it was much heavier on coal. At the end of the month it was returned to Nine Elms works and a number of minor changes were made: the blast pipe diameter was slightly lessened to give a sharper blast, the organ pipe was replaced by a standard type of whistle, and the livery was altered to the more usual London & South Western green. Back in service again, it continued to display its former faults; starting was difficult, steaming was erratic and coal consumption was immoderately high.

A leading article in *The Engineer* on 2 February 1900 described with comments a special journey made by No 720 at the head of a very heavy train, as observed from the footplate, and part of it is worth quoting:

'This type of engine is, we believe, the largest and most powerful in Great Britain. The tender is gigantic. It is nearly as high as the tops of the carriages, and holds over 4,000 gallons of water and five tons of coal. The train consisted of nineteen vehicles, most of them bogie coaches. The platform was crowded to its utmost capacity, for many had come to see friends and yet dearer ones off to South Africa [to fight in the Boer War] to say nothing of those crossing to New York. None too much room had been provided in the train, and at the last, just at the moment the locomotive was going to be hooked on, four large luggage vans crammed with mail bags had to be added. The total number of coaches thus became twenty-three, given in the official running sheet as 24½, and the gross weight behind the tender was 376½ tons, without passengers, luggage or mails. We shall not be far wrong if we take the total as 400 tons. The engine and tender weigh 96 tons. Viewed from the footplate, the train leaving the terminus "looked like the side of the street". The boiler pressure was 175 lbs and for the greater part of the run, made to Southampton without a station stop, the safety valves were on the point of blowing, or blowing lightly. The performance of the engine left nothing to be desired, and the consumption of coal was very moderate, as proved by the lengthened intervals between firing. The rate of running was extremely steady, post after post being passed at about forty-five miles an hour. For thirty miles out of the seventy-nine the run is all uphill, the line rising for seven continuous miles, on the Basingstoke and

> Woking section, at the rate of 1 in 249. Again, there are eleven miles, from the 20th mile on the Brookwood section, which rise continuously at the rate of 1 in 326, 314 and 304. Up the long bank through Basingstoke to the summit at Litchfield tunnel the speed fell off a little: no matter for wonder when the enormous weight of the train and the wind and the rain are considered. But, once over the hill, the engine was let to have her own way, and sixty miles an hour was reached and maintained with great ease. The putting on of the mail vans caused the train to start three minutes late, and four minutes were lost at Queens Road by permanent way signals, but it reached Southampton at 1.40 pm, thus making up time on the road, and we have not the least doubt that the running time could have been still further reduced had occasion demanded it.'

With a load of 400 tons (and probably more if the train was as full as alleged) on a two-hour schedule, this was admittedly not bad going, even though there were no fireworks. A net time of 113 minutes was creditable; one is, however, tempted to compare this performance with that of a 'School', No 932 *Blundells*, in August 1938, when a similar load was taken from Waterloo to Southampton in a net time of 81¾ minutes, the weight of the engine and tender being approximately the same at that of No 720. However, this was 38 years later with a superheated engine, at a time when the rolling resistances in carriage axleboxes were much less; the weather conditions were probably better as well. One notes that nothing is said about difficulty in starting; no doubt the engine which hauled the train into the platform at Waterloo also helped to push it out. The recorder also seemed to think that the consumption of coal was 'moderate'. This was a special occasion, and no doubt the footplatemen were hand-picked for their skill. However, it could by no means have been a typical performance. The fact was that No 720 was a failure, both in its original form and after the modifications it received later. I did *not* solve the 'heavy fast-train problem'.

During the two-and-a-quarter years between May 1900 and July 1902 this engine was out of service for ten whole months, undergoing alterations or repairs. In November 1903 it was taken into Nine Elms to await the fitting of a larger boiler. During the previous five years it had covered less than 74,000 miles. By now Drummond had launched upon the building of coupled 4-4-0s, the celebrated and successful 'Greyhounds', and the double-single idea had been given up.

It is surprising that, quite soon after No 720 was built, five more were constructed, differing in design only in details — though importantly in having the cylinder diameters reduced to 14 inches. Two other minor changes were the provision of inspection covers to facilitate access to the cross water tubes, and the widening of the splashers; the separate 'connecting rod splashers' now disappeared. Construction of these new engines began in 1899 and they entered traffic in the summer of 1901. They were numbered 369–373, and when new were first put on important expresses, but were later reserved for boat trains, troop

No 369, one of Drummond's subsequent batch of 'double singles', which differed from the prototype in having a larger boiler, wider wheel splashers and inspection covers on either side of the firebox which gave access to the cross-water tubes.
(NRM)

specials and secondary duties such as the service from Waterloo to Southampton by way of Alton, whose trains usually loaded to only four or five vehicles. Even so, their consumption of coal remained high. In a special test during the summer of 1905, after No 720 had been rebuilt with a large boiler along with the other five, it competed with two 'Greyhounds', and with similarly loaded trains both the latter performed better than the double-single, which showed itself unable to keep time and which burned 8 lb of coal per mile more. On fault which it displayed, now and at other times, was directly due to the non-provision of coupling rods. The inside cylinders, driving the front wheels, and the outside cylinders, driving the rear wheels, would get out of phase, and the result was an uneven pull on the drawbar. Indicator diagrams showed, too, that the cylinders, though all the same size, did not all do similar amounts of work. Even after being fitted with larger boilers, these engines also had difficulty in maintaining their steam pressure. The four cylinders, even though now reduced in capacity, were too thirsty for steam.

So these locomotives, of which such high hopes had originally been entertained, spent most of their working lives hauling lightly loaded semi-fast trains during the warmer months of the year, thus earning their nickname of 'Butterflies'. They lasted until the 1923 groupings, and two of them received the Southern livery. Now and then one might appear on an Ocean Liner Special of five or six carriages. By the middle of 1927 they had all been withdrawn. They were an interesting experiment. One wonders what would have been the result of coupling their wheels to prevent their cylinders getting out of phase. Possibly Drummond did not venture to do so because he distrusted existing metallurgical techniques and feared such a long coupling rod might snap in service. More likely he had shrugged off his earlier bright idea; faced with the need to build six-coupled engines to cope with increased loads, he did not think the experiment worth trying.

10

The Great Eastern 'Decapod'

The locomotives so far described were all unusual in one way or another, but none could be described as a monster. However, when a new tank locomotive appeared briefly on the Great Eastern Railway in 1903 it was as if a mammoth had suddenly been introduced into a zoo. Even so staid a periodical as *The Engineer* referred to it as 'enormous' and 'of vast size' — though by the standards of a quarter of a century later it was not all that large. It did not have a long life. It was built as an experiment and used for experimental purposes only; after that it vanished from public view, leaving only a memory behind.

When the present century began, the Great Eastern was facing the problem of how to transport the increasing numbers of season ticket holders who worked in the City of London and lived in its northern and eastern suburbs. They crowded the incoming morning and outgoing evening trains, filling them to bursting point. This was especially the case on the branch line that linked Liverpool Street and Enfield Town. It was not just a matter of providing sufficient seating accommodation and adequate standing room between the seats. To some extent that problem was in course of being solved. James Holden, the Company's Locomotive, Carriage and Wagon Superintendent, had begun to reconstruct many existing five-a-side compartment coaches, splitting them longitudinally down the middle and inserting a central section so that each compartment could now contain six seats a side. It was no doubt a tight fit, but at least passengers were not being subjected to sardine-tin conditions for very long at a stretch. The writer can testify that six-a-side seating in the compartment coaches of the Metropolitan Railway during the early 'thirties was not all that uncomfortable for an able-bodied teenager for up to 40 minutes, though it was a bother not to be able to stretch one's legs easily if one were seated, and by the time one reached Baker Street one was often glad of the opportunity to offer one's seat to a woman passenger — one did that sort of thing automatically in those days — and stand for the rest of the journey.

The real trouble was that Great Eastern suburban trains had, for reasons of platform length, to be about 320 tons in weight, and such a train could not accelerate rapidly when its motive power was a small 0-6-0 tank engine. There seemed to be a real likelihood of much traffic being lost to the new electric trams which were now grinding their vibratory ways along the middles of so many London streets, or even to the older horse-drawn omnibuses, both of which could accelerate more rapidly than a steam-hauled train even if they could not attain its maximum velocity. On a route like the one to Enfield Town, with 14 stops to be made in 10¾ miles, getting speed up *quickly* between stops mattered very much.

If the line were to be electrified, more passengers could certainly be carried in the speeded-up trains. Electric multiple units had superior accelerative abilities to existing steam locomotives, since for a short time the whole sequence of traction motors could be worked at maximum power without over-heating, so that a rate of 30 miles an hour could be attained from rest in half a minute. Such a solution, however, would be very expensive in first cost, requiring the provision of conductor rails or overhead wiring and a considerable investment in new rolling-stock.

Holden believed that the necessary acceleration could be achieved with steam, and began to make an extensive study of the possibilities. Among other things, he travelled over all the suburban lines of the system to see what the existing steam-hauled trains were actually doing, and how long they spent at station stops. (The latter turned out on average to be less than half a minute, so there was no point in trying merely to reduce them.) He then asked the Board of Directors for funds to be made available to build an experimental tank locomotive so as to find out whether the '30 miles an hour in 30 seconds' objective could be reached with a full train. Perhaps because the stakes were so high, the Directors agreed, though to construct such an engine would cost over £5,000.

Holden then set to work with his design team. There were two aims before them — the provision of the greatest possible tractive effort and the possession of a high adhesion weight. There were also limiting parameters — loading gauge restrictions and the maximum weight allowed by the Civil Engineer on the track for each pair of wheels. There was no need for high-speed capability, since there would be no opportunity for fast running when intermediate stops were so frequent.

It was first necessary to estimate what sort of machinery would provide an adequate pull at the drawbar — how many cylinders, and of what size; how many coupled wheels, and of what diameter? Since high speeds were in any case out of the question, a 0–10–0 wheel arrangement was decided on, each wheel to be 4 ft 6 in across. There were to be three cylinders, 18½ in by 24 in, the cranks being set at 120 degrees. The decision to employ an inside cylinder posed a problem which Holden solved in an ingenious manner. It was considered necessary for the pistons of all three cylinders to be in a horizontal line with the wheel-axles in order to achieve smooth running and even

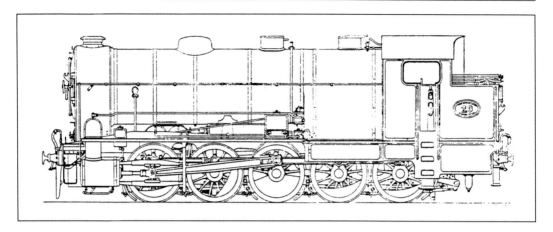

A drawing of J. Holden's 0-10-0 well tank engine, designed to accelerate rapidly with a 300-ton suburban train and match the expected performance of an electric multiple unit. Trials showed that it could reach 30 mph in 30 seconds from starting. However, it was considered too heavy for the branch line for which it had been intended, so it was never used in service.
(Railway Magazine)

balancing. The inside cylinder could not drive on the leading axle as there would not be enough space for the piston and connecting rods. So a means had to be found by which the inside connecting rod could turn a central crank on the second axle. The solution was to make it in the shape of a long isosceles triangle with a short base, so that there could be a hole in it through which the leading axle could pass. The leading axle was also slightly cranked so that it did not foul the connecting rod. The otherwise excessive weight of the latter was lessened by machining holes and gaps in it where this was safely possible.

So much for the moving parts: how now to supply the power? A very large boiler was obviously needed, with a firebox to match. The photograph of the engine shows its huge proportions — huge, that is, for its time. The boiler barrel was 5 ft 2 in in diameter internally and contained 395 steel tubes each 1¾ in wide; it was 15 ft 11 in long. The firebox was of the round-topped, wide-based type, and was the first of its kind to appear in Great Britain; the next example was to be seen on the first of the large-boilered Great Northern 'Atlantics', No 251, later in the same year, 1903. The grate was unusual; there were in fact three grates and three ashpans, the side pans being separated by some inches from the central pan; in this way space was found to spread the firebox over the frame and the coupled wheels. The boiler pressure was fixed at the then high figure of 200 lbs per square inch. No doubt with an eye to safety, as many as six safety valves were provided in two separate casings. The smokebox had unusual features; at the bottom, instead of the usual bed of bricks there was an inclined plate on which tiles were laid, and two circular doors were provided at the front base through which ashes could be raked out without the need to open the principal door. Also very unusual was the blast pipe from the cylinders, which had a central orifice of circular section surrounded by two annular pipes; the first took the central cylinder's exhaust, the others those from the outside cylinders.

Left *A three-quarter view of the 'Decapod' showing the unusually wide firebox, the two safety valve casings, the two circular doors for removing ash from the smokebox floor and the flat-sided covers on the outside cylinders which enabled them to fit within the loading gauge.* (LCGB)

Viewed from the side, besides the huge boiler and firebox and the diminutive dome and chimney, it was the wheels which caught the eye. The central coupled wheel on either side had a balance weight which extended inwards right to the hub. Had this been of iron or steel throughout it would not have been sufficiently heavy, but within outer steel retaining plates was a much heavier solid lead filling which made

Below *Sections across the firebox (seen from the rear) and across the smokebox (seen from the front) which show how closely the locomotive approached the limits of the loading gauge.* (The Engineer)

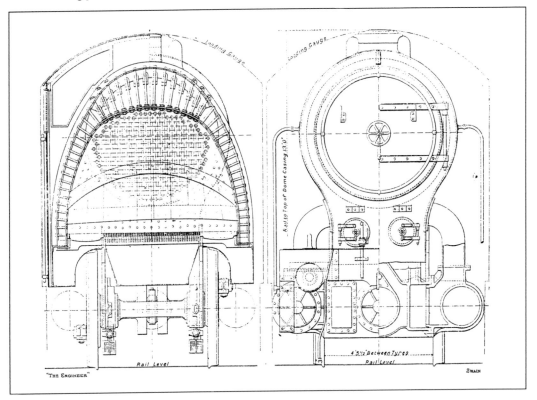

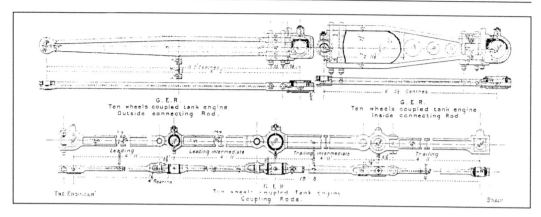

Diagrams of the connecting and coupling rods. Note the hole in the inside connecting rod (shaped like a round-topped door on its side) through which the axle of the front pair of coupled wheels passed. This enabled the cylinders to be positioned horizontally with the plane of the driving axles. (The Engineer)

an adequate balance possible. Four separate coupling rods on either side linked the wheels; each was jointed to permit up-and-down movement, and the rear joint also allowed for side movement, as the rear wheels were allowed a little play in their bearings. There were no flanges on the centre wheels. It was hoped that these devices would enable the easy rounding of curves. There were no side tanks, but a well tank was provided which held 1,500 gallons of water — not a great deal, but that did not matter when replenishment could be had at each end of a ten-mile journey. The bunker held two tons of coal. The cab, by Great Eastern standards, was a small one.

A special feature was the sanding apparatus. It was important for the locomotive to get a good grip on the rails when conditions were unfavourable; a wet or greasy rail would lessen the proportion of the total weight which would be available for adhesion. Two large air reservoirs were fixed beneath the boiler at the front end. One was for compressed air to work the Westinghouse brake, and the other was joined to it by a one-way valve. Air was pumped into both cylinders by the Westinghouse pump, the front cylinder receiving the air first. This cylinder supplied an air-blast to blow sand under the wheels, and the lever operating this blast was attached to the locomotive's regulator handle, so that when the driver deemed it necessary he could open the regulator and activate the sand-blast with the same arm movement. The non-return valve ensured that however much compressed air was lost from the sanding cylinder, there would be no loss of pressure in the brake cylinder.

Exactly what the locomotive weighed is something of a mystery. The figure put around at the time was 75 tons, but this appears to have been 'massaged' for the benefit of the Civil Engineer and others who might take alarm at the possibility of damage to the track. In working order the locomotive appears really to have weighed about 80 tons. This would have placed about 16 tons on each pair of coupled wheels, but the real trouble was that the wheels were so close together that the weight per foot of wheelbase would have been some 4 tons. This was greater than with any other locomotive in Great Britain before or since, and very much greater than was customary in 1903.

So much for the anatomy of this behemoth, remarkable in so many respects. It now had to be tested to see what sort of accelerative capacity it had. The times chosen for the trials were on Sunday mornings when traffic would be light, and the stretch of track selected was the main line between Chadwell Heath and Brentwood. Special timing equipment was set up along a distance of about a quarter of a mile along a short level section. A brush was fixed to the engine which touched in passing a number of equally spaced double electrical contacts and momentarily closed a circuit which enabled a pen to mark a paper strip moving at a uniform speed in a device housed in a hut at the side of the line. The variation of speed, and therefore the degree of acceleration, could be calculated from the decreasing distances between the marks on the paper.

Ken Nunn, the railway photographer to whom later rail enthusiasts are indebted for so many hundreds of pictorial records of steam locomotives and their trains, was at the time of the trials a schoolboy living near the Great Eastern main line. Later in his life, recalling the occasion, he wrote to a friend, in a letter now preserved in the Library of the National Railway Museum at York:

'I lived at Brentwood at the time of these trials, and have good reason to remember them, for I received one or two sound thrashings from my father on their account. No 20 arrived at Brentwood at about 11 o'clock on Sunday mornings, and after taking water ran around the train and shunted back into the up siding to follow the 2.26 pm local up (2 pm ex-Chelmsford). I was in the choir of the parish church at the time, and on these occasions there was usually a blank file in the choir stalls which I had reluctantly to explain when I reached home to a wrathful parent who had no soul for locomotives.

'There were five trips, all of which took place in 1903, and ran from Stratford on the following Sundays: 11 January, 8 February, 29 March, 26 April, 28 June ....

'The locomotive was required to lift from start an 18-coach suburban train, fully loaded and weighing 315 tons, and to attain a speed of 30 mph in 30 seconds, an acceleration of 1.46 feet per second. [Note: rate of change of speed is measured in *feet per second per second*, and this is what Nunn really means.] The necessary weight was obtained by placing butts of water and iron rails in the compartments of the vehicles.

'On the first trip (11 January) the engine gave priming troubles and ran only as far as Romford Factory, and the trial party returned home from there, but on all other occasions the trips were made to Brentwood.

'On the second trip (8 February) Brentwood was reached without mishap, but when running round her train No 20 took a large chunk out of the up platform at Brentwood station when negotiating the cross-over.

'On Sunday, 29 March, in a boisterous wind, and under somewhat adverse weather conditions, the engine registered an acceleration of 1.40 feet per second [per second] which was only six hundredths of a foot less than the desired figure, but it had on this occasion a 335-ton train, viz 20 tons heavier than the load stipulated.

'On the fourth trip (26 April) the speed of 30 mph was attained within the required time of 30 seconds, much to the delight of everybody, but I have no detail of the actual time in seconds or fractions thereof.

'The final and most intensive trials were run on 28 June, when four journeys each way were made by No 20, but again I have no details of these trips except that the load was a 335-ton train. On this occasion 12 other locomotives took part in these tests with the same load. They were:

Tender engines

Class Y14	No 647	0-6-0 Westinghouse fitted
Class T19 rebuilt	No 769	2-4-0 Belpaire firebox
Class N31	No 996	0-6-0 Westinghouse fitted 'Waterbury'
Class T19	No 1033	2-4-0 'standard (then unrebuilt)
Class F48	No 1189	0-6-0 Belpaire coal engine
Class F48	No 1187	0-6-0 non-Belpaire coal engine
Class T26	No 1257	2-4-0 'Intermediate'
Class S46	No 1860	4-4-0 'Claud Hamilton' non-Belpaire

Tank engines

Class R24	No 342	0-6-0T 'Jubilee' passenger
Class M15	No 659	2-4-2T Worsdell double-end passenger
Class C32	No 1040	2-4-2T Holden condensing local passenger
Class S44	No 1131	0-4-4T Holden front-coupled suburban passenger

Harry Dorrington was the driver of No 20 on all these trips.'

It is not clear from Ken Nunn's narrative why it was thought necessary to test all these other locomotives, but possibly Holden wished to establish that no other engine was capable of achieving the necessary acceleration. No 20, it seems, could do so but only succeeded on its fourth attempt. Dr W.A. Tuplin, in an article in *Railway World*, August 1964, suggests that in its original state it was not up to its requirement to accelerate at 1.46 feet per second per second, and that at some time before the fourth test an unpublicized adjustment was made to the safety valves on the boiler, permitting the pressure to rise to 250 lbs per square inch. This would have increased the engine's tractive effort by a quarter as much again, so that what was almost achieved in March could be managed easily a month later. It seems likely that Tuplin was right, and that the 'Decapod' was the first British steam locomotive to have a boiler pressed to so high a figure.

So the new engine could have been rated a success — but Nemesis, in the shape of the Civil Engineer, was waiting in the wings. He declared that No 20 could not be used on the line for which it was intended because so large a part of the track ran across brick arches. One would have thought that this was an objection which could have been made before the engine was built, but possibly news of the difference between the stated and actual weights had leaked out. Holden did not take it very well. According to Ken Nunn:

'He was very peeved over the whole affair and when he retired at the end of 1907 he ordered quite a lot of stuff to be handed over to him personally, and with it went a large number of official negatives. I think he did not intend that anyone else should benefit by his experience.'

After its successful performances in April and June 1903, the locomotive returned to Stratford works and spent some years there covered up with tarpaulins. Eventually Holden was told that he could make what use of it he liked, and some of its parts were employed in the construction of a two cylinder 0–8–0 freight engine which plied on goods trains to and from March in Cambridgeshire for a while. It was scrapped following the 1923 groupings.

It remains to explain why the Great Eastern did not go on to introduce electrification, since the Civil Engineer could have had no objection to multiple unit electric trains on the Enfield or any other branch. It seems that the expected growth of traffic on the inner suburban lines did not in fact occur. Electric trams were now being used more widely on the roads in and around London, and for short journeys they were found more convenient. Season ticket holders continued to travel in their packed carriages behind sturdy little 0–6–0 tank engines only half as powerful as the 'Decapod', but the overcrowding did not get any worse. It was some 60 years before routes into Liverpool Street were electrified — and now, nearly 90 years after the building of Holden's challenger, every train leaving that terminus is electrically powered.

The 'Decapod' as rebuilt into a 0-8-0 goods engine. Little was left of the original engine apart from two of the three cylinders and eight of the ten driving wheels. Note the outside steam pipe to the cylinder. (LCGB)

11

The rise and fall of the steam rail-motor

During the earlier years of the twentieth century there occurred an interesting though short-lived episode in British railway history: the rise and fall of the steam rail-motor. It flowered briefly on most of the main-line companies' branch lines and on some of the lesser lines both in Great Britain and Ireland. The conditions favouring the appearance of these vehicles lasted only for a short while, so that like Robert Herrick's daffodils they hasted away too soon; unlike Wordsworth's daffodils there were never as many as ten thousand of them, but until the outbreak of the First World War they were pretty numerous. After they had passed from the scene a certain number of steam railcars of a completely different design were built by private firms and two British railway companies bought some; a brief resumé of them and their uses is given at the end of this chapter, though they do not strictly fall within the remit of this book since they did not originate from any of the railway companies and were not the products of their workshops.

The typical steam rail-motor, as built during the earlier years of the twentieth century, was a single midget locomotive permanently attached to a single vehicle and intended for operation on lightly used sections of line, usually on suburban or country branches, where a single coach was sufficient to meet demand. Basically it was an economy measure. The railway still provided the only convenient mode of public transport in sparsely populated areas which happened to be served by a line — and a glance at a pre-grouping railway map of Great Britain will show how many secondary and branch lines then existed, which are now growing grass or have been built over. The ubiquitous motor-bus powered by an internal combustion engine was as yet hardly to be seen. Horse-drawn omnibuses and wagonettes were few and slow. Private cars were very much the preserve of the wealthy. So, though in many cases they did not pay their ways, existing railway routes were kept in being. Public use of them varied very much, both throughout the day and seasonally. The coach of a rail-motor might be filled during morning and evening services and only sparsely occupied at other times. There was no point in reserving a whole locomotive to haul a single coach on such services when the former might weigh more than the latter, and when it would be standing idle for long intervals between

short journeys, consuming fuel all the time since the fire had to be kept alight.

The conception of a small locomotive inseparably attached to its single coach in a sort of monogamous marriage was not an entirely new one in the early 1900s. James Samuel, at that time Chief Locomotive Engineer of the Eastern Counties Railway, designed and caused to be built by a private firm a small unit weighing altogether a little over three tons, which actually ran as far as Cambridge from the Company's terminus at Shoreditch in 1847, and when on trial reached a speed of 47 miles an hour. The passenger accommodation was a sort of truck with benches set all round the interior; it had no door; and to enter it one climbed over the side. In front of the seat area a small vertical boiler provided steam for two tiny cylinders beneath the floor, 3½ in by 6 in,

A Great Northern Railway steam rail-motor, of typical construction, built by H.A. Ivatt, with four coupled wheels and a squat, forward-facing boiler. (NRM)

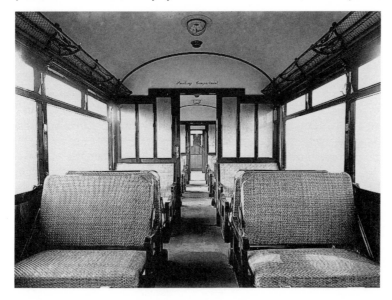

Interior view of the GNR rail-motor shown above. The seat backs were reversible. (NRM)

which drove the front pair of wheels. Everything else was similarly proportioned. It never carried any fare-paying passengers, but was used to transport railway officials for a few years and then vanished into limbo. Samuel built another and larger vehicle in 1848 which had covered-in passenger accommodation carried on four wheels, which were outside and not beneath the coach body, and a two-wheeled motor unit in which the cylinders beneath the boiler, which was vertical, drove backwards on to a jack-shaft from which the driving wheels were worked by external coupling rods, one on either side. Built originally for the Eastern Counties Railway, it was sold in 1849 to the Bristol & Exeter Railway, which adapted it to the broad gauge and used it for some years between Tiverton Junction and Tiverton before scrapping the coach and rebuilding the engine as a 2–2–2. One or two more such units were later built by Samuel for branch line work but none appears to have been a success.

The idea re-surfaced in 1902 and, for reasons indicated above, was widely developed on all English main lines except the Great Eastern and North Eastern. In Scotland the Glasgow & South Western and the Great North of Scotland built some, while in Wales many of the smaller Welsh companies also constructed some, notably the Taff Vale Railway. The chief Irish companies, except for the Midland & Great Western, also experimented with them. Along with the introduction of such units went the establishment of un-manned halts between existing stations, at which only the rail-motors would stop, and the issue and collection of tickets by the guard. In this way it was hoped to maximize passenger patronage while at the same time effecting economies. Signalling could be dispensed with on branches run on the 'one engine in steam' principle, and there was no need for turntables since rail-motor units were intended to be operated from either end. The driver, when at the

A Lancashire & Yorkshire steam rail-motor of typical design. Note the steps needed for passengers to board it from low platform halts, and the long handrails beside them. (NRM)

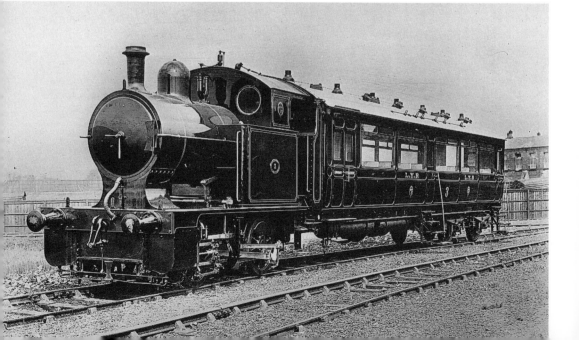

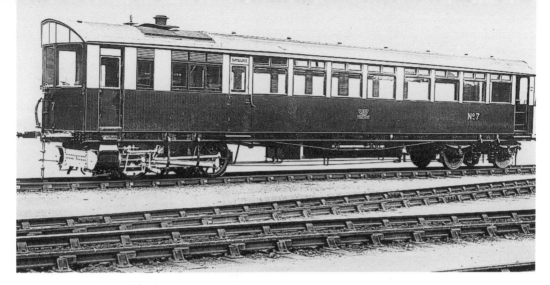

coach end, with the locomotive pushing the train, worked the controls mechanically through rods or chains which passed along the roof of the coach, and communicated with the fireman through a speaking tube or by code messages on a bell. Some units had the locomotive enclosed within the coach, its wheels in effect forming a powered coach-bogie; usually locomotive and coach were articulated to each other.

With a unit of this sort there was no call for high speed (too many stops had to be made for that to be possible) and no need either for large storage spaces for coal and water; a small bunker in the cab sufficed for a ton or so of the former, and a well-tank or, exceptionally, small side tanks provided the latter. Most rail-motors built for British lines had short horizontal boilers parallel with the frames, but a few had transverse or vertical ones. The firebox could not be re-charged when the locomotive was actually exhausting steam, as the draught would then expel much unburnt fuel from the chimney since the boiler tubes were so short. Accordingly, firing could only be done when the engine was free-wheeling down a gradient or when it was standing at a station or halt, which was of course quite often. From the railway company's point of view it was a disadvantage that the fireman had always to be a 'passed fireman', on a slightly higher wage scale than an ordinary fireman, since when his mate was at the other end of the unit he often had to perform operations proper to a driver. From the driver's viewpoint the work was attractive if he was approaching the end of his working life. It was far less onerous than driving trains along a busy main line, and transference to this kind of duty during the last year or so of his railway service was often valued as a kind of sheltered backwater immediately before retirement.

The steam rail-motor suffered from two built-in defects which would probably have led to its being superseded or radically re-designed if international events had not supervened. One was a lack of power. The locomotive *had* to be small for reasons of economy, and could easily be too small. It was designed to haul only a single coach, and if that coach

Great Western Railway rail-motor No 7. The locomotive is enclosed within the coachwork and has a vertical boiler and coupled driving wheels. The driving position at either end faces directly forwards through end windows. (NRM)

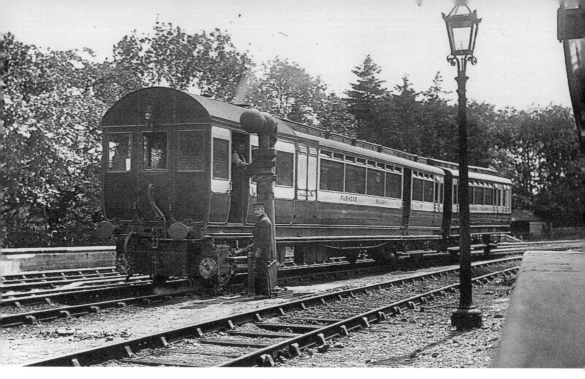

happened to be overloaded it might scarcely be able to pull it at all. To take an actual example: in 1902 Dugald Drummond designed and built a steam rail-motor for the short branch between Fratton and East Southsea, not quite two miles long and jointly owned by the London & South Western and London, Brighton & South Coast Railways. It was sent to the Great Western Railway to be tested, and the latter, after trying it out on a more or less level stretch of line, returned it with a favourable report. It was put to work at once on the East Southsea branch, and was immediately found to be too weak to climb the slight gradients when it was filled with passengers. Enquiries made to Swindon established that it had been empty when tested. Fifty passengers — a mere 3 or 4 tons over and above the total weight of the vehicle — were enough to make the engine stall. It had to be taken out of service and re-designed with a bigger boiler and larger cylinders before it could do its job. Rail-motors had to be tailor-made to suit the conditions on the route for which they were designated if they were to be reliable as well as economical.

Another built-in defect was the noise made when travelling, accompanied by the marked oscillation as the pistons thumped to and fro. Since the coach was attached to the engine through articulation, or alternatively the engine was the coach bogie at one end, the rattle and vibration to which the footplate crew were inured were also passed on to the passengers in the coach, which (except in the first class portion, if there were one) was frequently lacking in upholstery which could cushion the blows. A journey in a steam rail-motor could be very uncomfortable and deter intending travellers if there were any other means of travel available.

It was the First World War that sounded the death-knell for the type of steam rail-motor used so widely in Edwardian times. The need for such units lessened greatly under wartime conditions, especially during 1917–18, so that on most lines they were withdrawn and either put into store or broken up. When the War ended many were found to be unusable. Only on the Great Western, Great Northern, London & North Western and Lancashire & Yorkshire Railways was it found possible to keep them operating during the war years. Those few which did survive lingered on into the post-grouping period. One Lancashire & Yorkshire unit just managed to survive until the formation of British Railways, being scrapped in March 1948. The idea itself, however, did not die; railcars built on a quite different pattern were constructed and used in the 'twenties and 'thirties, as related later in this chapter.

The whole 'rise and fall' episode could in itself be regarded as a lengthy experiment with steam. It would be tedious to describe even briefly all the various examples of rail-motors built during the Edwardian period. One example has been selected in which an unusual type of vertical boiler was tried out, giving rise to an unusual external appearance. Of it, one is fortunate to have some splendid photographs as well as a contemporary newspaper report of how it was seen by its users when first introduced.

The experience of the most northerly line in Great Britain to experiment with steam rail-motors proved to be a brief engagement followed by an abrupt jilting. The Great North of Scotland Railway ranked somewhere between a minor and a major company. It had a corner of Scotland all to itself and operated a considerable passenger traffic on lines which linked Aberdeen with Peterhead, Fraserburgh and Elgin, plied along the Banff and Moray coasts and ventured into the foothills of the Cairngorms in search of cargoes of whisky; it also operated the Deeside branch which regularly carried Royal Trains to Balmoral. Two small offshoots, from Fraserburgh and Elgin respectively, served the golfing resort of St Combs and the small port of Lossiemouth. This line had the special distinction of operating nearly all its traffic with handsome 4–4–0s with moderately small driving wheels

Dugald Drummond's steam rail-motor for the East Southsea branch, as originally designed. It proved too weak to tackle one gradient on the branch when fully loaded, and had to be reconstructed. (NRM)

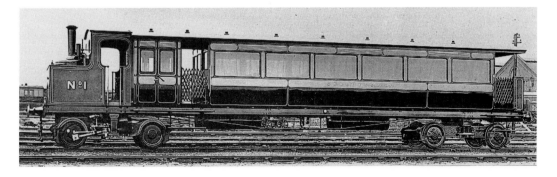

and (alone in Scotland) cabs of ample size for the benefit of the locomotive crews.

The St Combs branch was opened in 1903, and possibly it was this which caused the directors of the company to debate at considerable length the question of whether or not to go in for steam rail-motors on this branch and the one to Lossiemouth. The debate continued through two sessions and in January 1904 it was decided to invite tenders for two such units. The following September the quotation from Andrew Barclay and Company, of Kilmarnock, was accepted for the 'steam motor-car bogie' (as the specification termed it) alone. The coach body was to be constructed at the company's carriage works at Inverurie.

The specification itself, which makes interesting reading, appears to indicate that the decision to use vertical boiler was an afterthought, presumably of the Locomotive Superintendent W. Pickersgill, since the words 'with Cochran-type boiler' were written in ink under the typed heading, and the actual specification for the boiler comes right at the end of the document. The Cochran boiler, which had been successfully used on stationary plants, had never before been employed in a locomotive. It was essentially a wide cylindrical drum, whose lower end had the firebox recessed into it, and whose upper end was not flat but hemispherical, acting as an enormous steam dome. Hot gases from the firebox passed up one side and then traversed laterally arranged tubes, afterwards being directed to the smokebox in front, and so to the chimney. One advantage of this type of boiler, as applied to a locomotive, was that it could be made very wide without obscuring the driver's view forward, since he looked not along the barrel but past its hemispherical top. The lower part of it was pressed out of a single piece of sheet metal, so that no bolts or rivets came into contact with the fire. The steam regulator was fixed within the hemispherical top.

The cylinders, 10 in by 16 in, attached below the cab, drove forwards on to the front wheels; the outside valve gear was a diminutive version of the Walschaerts type. Two safety valves projected upwards from the domed portion of the boiler close to the cab front. A bunker holding three-quarters of a ton of coal was attached to the front of the coach body, while beneath it, underneath the forward part of the coach, was a water tank holding 650 gallons.

The coach itself was articulated to the locomotive. It held 46 passengers, third class only, a door at the rear on either side giving access to the passenger saloon and also to the driver when the unit was to be driven with the engine at the rear. The saloon's interior made no concessions to the flesh; it was bare and had hard slatted wooden seats with reversible backs. The driver's controls at the rear end included a ship's telegraph appliance for operating the instruments in the cab, the regulator valve being worked by a system of rods and levers. The Westinghouse brake could be operated from either end.

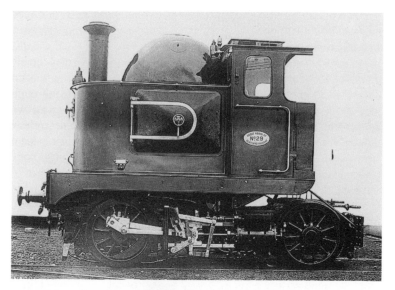

The locomotive component of the GNSR rail-motor, taken at Andrew Barclay's works, Kilmarnock, showing the huge hemispherical top of the Cochran-type boiler. The hinged side doors on either side gave access to the fire tubes which traversed the lower part of the boiler from left to right. (Glasgow University)

Front view of the locomotive component of the GNSR steam rail-motor. (Glasgow University)

When on test near Inverurie, the unit showed it could accelerate to 30 miles an hour in 20 seconds, and a maximum speed of 60 miles an hour was attained — a figure seldom reached by any train on the Great North of Scotland system and about twice what was needed on the branches to which the units were to be sent. However, they quickly proved unacceptable in daily service. The chief trouble was the noise they made and the accompanying vibration, which made even the 20-minutes-at-most of each branch line journey something to be endured rather than enjoyed. Also, despite their out-sized boilers, they did not steam well. Introduced on both branches in November 1905, they were taken off again a year later, the coach bodies then being converted to separate saloon vehicles — and, one trusts, made somewhat more comfortable. The locomotives themselves were stored and eventually, in 1910, offered for sale. There were no takers, so in 1912 they were broken up — a sad end to an interesting experiment.

When the one intended to work to Lossiemouth was sent to Elgin, the *Northern Scot and Moray & Nairn Express* in its issue of 6 November 1905 included an article on it, largely quoted below:

'NEW RAILWAY DEPARTURE AT ELGIN
STEAM RAIL CAR TO AND FROM LOSSIEMOUTH

Passengers travelling from Elgin to Lossiemouth and *vice versa* will in future be conveyed by a steam rail car. This new departure in railway locomotion was initiated by the Great North of Scotland Railway Company on Wednesday [ie on the previous 1 November] and by no stretch of imagination could it be said that the engine proper is a thing of beauty. Its shape is peculiar in the extreme but it can apparently do its work. The locomotive stands on four coupled wheels[1] and the boiler, instead of being cylindrical, is spherical.[2] A huge dome [ie the boiler top], which detracts greatly from the symmetry of the engine, surmounts the boiler close to the cab, which is large and roomy. To the locomotive is attached a car of large dimensions. The exterior presents a saloon appearance, while the inside is something of the nature of the top of a tramway car. It runs very smoothly on two bogeys and is comfortably upholstered.[3] Entrance is had by one door and a corridor leads up the centre of the coach. It can accommodate forty-six passengers ... It has been an object of much interest during the last few days, its smooth running qualities[4] making up for what it lacks in beauty ...'

1   Whoever was sent to view the unit does not seem to have been very observant. The wheels were *not* coupled. Possibly it was inspected when standing at the platform, when the error could have been made through looking down at the valve gear mechanism and mistaking what was seen.

2   A mistaken deduction, probably the result of merely looking at the hemispherical top.

3   It is obvious that the reporter never looked through the windows of the vehicle, let alone entering it. By no stretch of imagination (his own phrase) could wooden slatted seats be regarded as comfortable upholstery.

4   One wonders what made him think it ran smoothly. He clearly never travelled in it before writing his piece. Its poor running qualities were the main reason for its later withdrawal.

Three more paragraphs in the same issue added to the story:

'A LOSSIEMOUTH VIEW OF IT

Previous to the past few years passengers bound for Lossie arriving at Elgin had nothing to do but look for the Lossie engine, and they knew they were right. Of late, however, with the new station at Elgin and the strange engines on the trains, it was not so easy ferreting out the Lossie platform, and had not Providence spared William Paul, the "gaird", Lossie loons returning to the old place would actually have to "speir the wye hame". Unless more of the new sort of trains are put on, Lossie loons will now easily know where to go. The new engine forms part of a large open carriage, which contains a double row of seats running along from end to end ... A fine view is got from the gable end of the new carriage coming down, and the only bad results to be anticipated are the effects on nervous people when Mrs A's hens or Mrs B's cat strays upon the line — or, more serious still, if by any chance a Seatown mongrel ... is lured into comparative safety by the innocent look of the approaching vehicle, comes into contact with the wheel and meets a premature death. We shall, however, hope for the best.'

Perhaps, when the units were withdrawn twelve months later, the orchestra of noise having become more than anyone could bear, the locals reflected that this, too, was for the best.

When steam rail-motors of the pre-war type vanished from the scene after the First World War, their saga was to have a sequel, though the inspiration for a new breed did not come from the railway companies themselves but from an independent engineering firm, the Sentinel Waggon Works at Shrewsbury. Steam on branch lines was not yet quite ready to give up the ghost. When the third decade of the present century opened, although competition from petrol- or diesel-driven road vehicles was something with which railways had to reckon, it was by no means clear that the former were going to take a great part of the latter's traffic away. In 1920 no branch line had yet had to close — indeed, there was one which had not yet been opened, the Torrington and Halwill Junction line in North Devon and Cornwall.

In regard to road transport generally, long-distance coaches scarcely existed; petrol-driven omnibuses plied only locally; many roads which

The Great North of Scotland's steam rail-motor which plied between Elgin and Lossiemouth. The engine was articulated to its coach and drove the front pair of wheels only.
(Scottish Record Office)

have long since been widened and improved were then just narrow lanes which large vehicles could only negotiate with difficulty; and a general speed limit of 30 miles an hour obtained for all traffic. Only a very few families had a private car at their disposal. So, if there were a railway handy, one used it, both for commuting to work, making short local journeys or going on holiday.

Though the writing was not yet on the wall, potentially the threat was there. Branch lines operated with trains of old carriages hauled by old locomotives. Because of the very low wage payable to train crews and to railway employees generally, the wastefulness of the steam branch line services did not show up too badly yet in company balance sheets. But a few far-sighted persons could see what was coming, and the Sentinel Waggon Works was one of them. It had begun by making steam road vehicles, and early in the 'twenties began to apply its expertise to building a new type of steam railcar that would allow a railway to carry short-distance passengers more cheaply than was possible with a locomotive-hauled train. Its publicity hand-outs made the point that railways lost valuable traffic because they could not economically cater for the short-distance movement of passengers and freight, and that their company was offering units which could make such traffic possible and prevent it from being sent by road. They had developed a type of miniature steam traction unit which needed a smaller boiler than the traditional sort, using a different method of boiling water, and had a more compact engine; both could be fitted into one end of a vehicle and constructed lightly to save weight, or alternatively they could be fitted within a smaller vehicle and do shunting work. The latter development is not, however, dealt with here for reasons of space.

The boiler was of the water-tube variety, now being used in the engine rooms of steamships and on stationary engines in increasing numbers. (More will be said about this type of boiler below, in chapter 18). In the Sentinel Patent Boiler, the fire heated the water in the tubes which supplied steam to a drum which surrounded the pipes in a hollow shell. Above the pipes was a superheater for the steam. The whole boiler unit was extremely compact, being less than 5 feet in height and only 4 feet wide. The fire below the tubes played radiant heat upon them and gases of combustion passed between the tubes to heat the superheater elements, and thence mixed with the steam from the blast pipe to reach the exterior through a chimney that projected upwards through the vehicle's roof. The boiler pressures were high; 230 lbs per square inch in the earlier railcars, 300 in the more powerful later ones. The smaller boilers were fired from above through a coal-chute; the larger ones used later were too high for this to be possible, so a fire door was installed just above the grate.

The Sentinel Patent Engine differed very much from the ordinary cylinders-and-motion of the conventional steam locomotive. In the earlier models it was upright (though later models had cylinders, piston rods and connecting rods horizontal with the frames). Secondly, its cylinders, like those of the Paget and Uniflow engines to be described later, had separate ports for entry and exit of steam. Thirdly, the valve gear was of the poppet type, worked by cams which operated through push-rods. The controls allowed for five valve-settings — two forward, two backward and a central one that held all valves open so that steam could be blown through the cylinders to warm the engine up. Fourthly, the feed water was continuously being injected into the boiler by the engine, being first pre-heated by exhaust steam. Fifthly, the whole engine below the level of the cylinders was enclosed in a crank case with an oil bath. Sixthly, and perhaps most unusually, the engine was designed to run much faster than that of any other steam locomotive; its maximum speed was 500 revolutions a minute, a chain drive or gearing being used to reduce the speed of the wheel-axle.

The first Sentinel Railcar, built in collaboration with Messrs Cammell Laird of Nottingham, who constructed the body, was built for the 3 ft 6 in gauge Jersey Railways and Tramways. The coach was articulated to the frame of the engine, and its wheels were built up from rubber between the hubs and rims to make for quieter running. It had both hand and steam brakes, electric lighting from an axle-driven dynamo and batteries, and gearing to permit 20 miles-an-hour running. There were seats for 44 second class and 12 first class passengers. The line on which it was to be run was 3¾ miles long, with six intermediate stops; the time allowed was a quarter of an hour. It became almost a tourist attraction in itself. Unlike the earlier steam rail-motors, it ran more smoothly than the trains which had preceded it, and people now tended to avoid these and use the new railcar — so much so that it was often required to carry as many standing as seated passengers. Its success was

Plan and side elevation of the Sentinel-Cammell steam railcar built in 1922 for Jersey Railways.

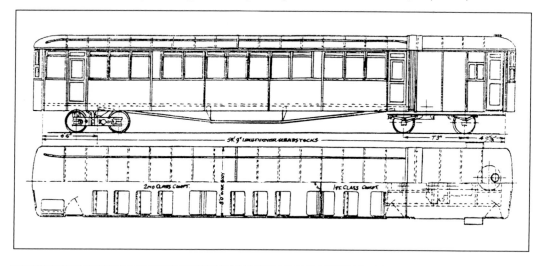

such that a second unit was ordered, and then, three years later in 1925, a third. The result was that the locomotives and coaches whose places they had taken became redundant and disappeared.

The Sentinel-Cammell railcar was subsequently marketed to many overseas countries; in this country the London, Midland & Scottish and London & North Eastern Railways bought quite a number for short-distance stopping trains and branch-line duties; these of course were for the standard gauge and larger than the Jersey railcar, and in some cases were units of two coaches. They were used successfully until the eve of the Second World War. The London & North Eastern painted theirs in distinctive colours and named them after stage-coaches of the past.

Front view of a London & North Eastern Railway Sentinel-Cammell steam railcar, taken at York. It plied on the coastal line between Scarborough, Whitby and Saltburn in NE Yorkshire, and proved itself able to cope with gradients of 1 in 40. (NRM)

However, the Sentinel-Cammell cars did not survive the Second World War, and despite the economies they achieved probably could not have lasted much longer in any case once the private car, the long-distance motor lorry and the motor coach began to use the roads. They were not as economical to use as the latter. In the first place, they needed coal for fuel; this was becoming increasingly expensive and a separate fireman was needed on any steam-driven unit as well as a driver, to fuel the fire. In the second place, the lines on which they had travelled in the 'thirties were being closed in the 'fifties, in order to reduce costs to the railway. When they had disappeared, the diesel multiple units took their places on whatever branch lines were left. With their disappearance the second and last act of the railcar story in this country ended.

Interior of the LNER Sentinel-Cammell railcar shown opposite, looking towards the rear-end driving compartment. Note the straps for standing passengers. The vehicle was intended to hold up to 70 people. (NRM)

12

The Paget locomotive

While the Decapod was demonstrating its accelerative capabilities on the Great Eastern main line and steam rail-motors were multiplying their numbers in all parts of the country, another type of engine, unusual in quite a different way, was taking shape in the mind of a Midland Railway engineer who, at the age of 30, had already become Works Manager at Derby.

Cecil Paget was the son of the Chairman of the Midland Railway Company. Possibly his parentage may have had something to do with his being appointed to a high position at such an early age, but his personal qualities must also have had a part. As a boy he had been sent to Harrow School, where his high intelligence misapplied itself in various ingenious ways of infringing or evading school rules and regulations which, so it was said, resulted in his being corporally chastised more frequently than anyone before or since. Kenneth Leech, writing in the *Railway Gazette* on 2 November 1945, mentions an incident after he had left school:

> 'The story of his encounter, when an undergraduate, with his old Headmaster, Dr Welldon, is possibly apocryphal. "I'm Paget, Sir; perhaps you don't remember me?" "Oh, yes, I do, Paget, but your face is perhaps not the feature I should remember best.'

After leaving Harrow he was apprenticed at Derby, left for a period of study at Cambridge University and returned again to pass rapidly upwards into the higher official ranks, excessive youthful exuberance having now matured, as with Henry V and Shakespeare, into great professional competence and an intelligent interest in his work which spilled over into his spare time.

During his stay at Cambridge he had learned about a type of stationary steam engine, the 'Willans Central Valve System', which was being successfully applied to the generation of electricity in all parts of the country; it relied for its steam distribution on a rotary valve instead of on the usual reciprocating type. If it could work on a stationary plant, why not on a locomotive? Possibly Paget made attempts to have his ideas tried out officially; if so, equally possibly his reputation as a former prankster and perhaps also some resentment because he had influence behind him, militated against his being taken seriously. So, having private funds at his disposal, he determined to build at his own expense the locomotive whose shape and substance were forming in his mind.

He obtained the use of a small office close to Derby station, engaged two young engineers, James Clayton and Herbert Chambers, as full-time assistants to do the detailed work of designing, and came to advise and consult them during the evenings when he was free. In this way the drawings for the Paget locomotive were produced from the autumn of 1904 onwards.

Paget's aim was to produce an all-purpose locomotive, something analogous to Sir William Stanier's later highly successful mixed traffic 'Black Five' 4-6-0, which could perform with equal ability on both fast passenger and slow heavy freight trains, thus eventually making redundant many different types of locomotive which had been tailored to the performance of particular duties. The Midland Railway had a large mineral traffic; hence the many goods trains which ambled along its slow roads behind 0-6-0s which were to be seen everywhere. It also had passenger services that ranged between London, Bristol and Birmingham in the south and west to Sheffield, Manchester, Leeds and Carlisle in the north and east. These were mostly worked by 4-4-0s of one kind or another, with Mr Johnson's 4-2-2s taking a hand with the lighter trains. Passenger loadings were as a matter of policy kept light. If Paget's engine could have been successfully developed it would probably have performed both duties efficiently and pulled heavier passenger trains into the bargain. Its use could well have resulted in many economies. But genius is a quality in short supply among human beings, and Paget was the only high official on the Midland Railway to possess it. The company had an able, if somewhat short-tempered, Locomotive Superintendent in Robert Deeley, but he was evidently not receptive to Paget's proposed innovations — for the engine which the latter was proposing to build had more than one completely new element in its make-up.

The preliminary designing took about three years, and during this time a number of changes were made to the original idea — such as giving the engine a 2-6-2 wheel arrangement. Actual construction then began — and Paget ran out of funds. The company agreed to take the venture over, but only on condition that it, not Paget, should undertake the tests, and that there was to be a limit to any experimental work which might subsequently need to be carried out. At some point in 1908 (an exact chronology is lacking) the engine was completed. What then followed was a melancholy anti-climax after the high hopes which its three designers had entertained.

No 2299 was, in external appearance, quite an impressive machine, though not outrageously different from the usual run of locomotives. To the outside observer, only the wide-based, round-topped firebox, the fact that the boiler was slightly wider than the smokebox and the unusual backward extension of the coupling rods on either side would have seemed out of the ordinary. Chimney, cab and tender were all

Above *Cecil Paget's 2-6-2 experimental locomotive. Note the inside frames and outside springing, the large boiler and wide firebox with lugs for lifting, and the backward extension of the coupling rod to drive the crank axle which operated the valve gear. (NRM)*

reminiscent of contemporary Midland practice. The innovations comprised a firebox of quite unusual design; eight inside cylinders of very short stroke; trunk pistons with no piston rods or slide bars, whose thrust was in only one direction; rotary sleeve-valves for distributing steam in place of the usual reciprocating type; and a longitudinal shaft worked from the coupling rods through a gear box to turn the rotary valves. These were all in addition to a number of minor changes from established practice.

The boiler was unusually large for its time, the front ring being 6 ft 6½

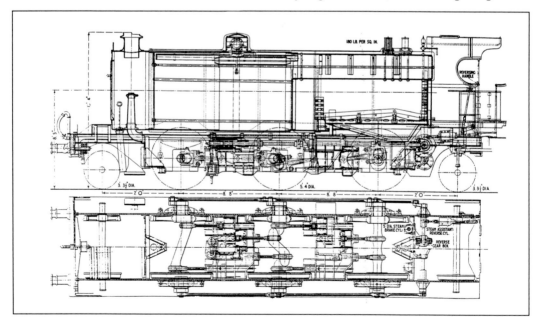

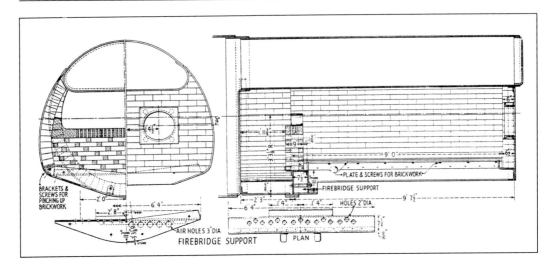

in wide internally and the rear ring 6 ft 8 in. No information exists as to the number of fire tubes in it. The firebox was almost as long as the tubed part of the boiler and had 55 square feet of grate area. It was unique in that the sides, back wall and cross-bridge (there was no brick arch) were entirely of bricks — 9 inches thick in the case of the cross-bridge and 6 inches thick elsewhere. The only part, therefore, which needed to be stayed was the crown. It passed heat to the boiler water only through the crown and by way of the tube-plate and tubes, but this was amply sufficient. There were two fire doors side by side, a self-cleaning ashpan and suitably placed nozzles by means of which jets of hot water from the injector system could flush out the ashes and unburnt remains after the engine had returned to the shed. Air supply to the grate was assisted by two side-scoops outside the frames which had doors under the fireman's control. The boiler had four lugs, clearly visible in the photograph, to enable it to be easily lifted or lowered. The six coupled wheels were each 5 ft 4 in wide, and the coupling rods were outside the frames.

The eight cylinders, all within the frames, were arranged in two groups of four, each group being a separate casting which included the steam chest and each being placed on either wide of the middle driving axle. Two cylinders in each group faced forwards and two backwards, so that the middle axle had four cranks and the front and rear ones two each. The stroke was only 12 inches. A peculiarity of each pair of cylinders on either side in each casting was that they communicated with each other, their backs to some extent overlapping and with no division at the overlap, so that when steam was admitted it entered two cylinders at the same moment; thus one admission valve serving both was sufficient. At each end of the stroke a ring of exhaust ports on the inside of each cylinder was exposed, and the steam escaped through

Arrangement of the firebox brickwork and the brick firebridge in the Paget locomotive. There were two fire doors with their centres 29 inches apart. (The Railway Gazette)

Left *Diagram showing the general arrangement of parts in the Paget locomotive, and the plan showing the positions of the eight trunk cylinders below the boiler and firebox. (The Railway Gazette)*

them. Since each piston acted in one direction only, the eight-cylinder arrangement was the equivalent of four double-acting cylinders. Each of the pistons was directly jointed to a short connecting rod which turned the crank; there were no piston rods and no slidebars.

The valve gear needed no eccentrics and had no reciprocating parts. The valves were cylinders, each centrally placed above one of the two groups of four cylinders, and each contained a revolving sleeve inside a liner which moved forwards or backwards and admitted steam from the steam chests to the cylinders through ports in the liner. Each sleeve was rotated by a shaft that extended along the locomotive's centre line and was itself driven through a cross-axle with a rank at each end outside the framing; this in turn was rotated by a backward extension from each coupling rod. An epicyclic gearbox transmitted the movement of the cross-axle to the shaft that operated the valve sleeves, and also provided for its reversal.

Alteration of the cut-off was achieved through the movable brass liner that enclosed each sleeve valve, which could be adjusted to present one, two, three or four ports for the passage of steam through the valves into the cylinders, cutting off respectively at 25½, 42, 59 and 75 per cent of full stroke. It was worked from the cab by means of three handles; one selected either forward or rearward movement, another admitted steam to work a cylinder which moved the liners through hydraulic pressure (much as a foot-pedal works the brakes in a car) and the third altered the degree of cut-off. Thus no great physical effort was required on the footplate.

The finished locomotive was given trials on the main line between Derby and Leicester, and proved it could exceed 80 miles an hour with a fully-loaded test train. The boiler behaved satisfactorily and steamed well; apart from the cracking of a few bricks, the firebox, too, gave no trouble. Things went wrong with the valves, however, because of differential expansion in the different metals used. Many slight changes in dimensions needed to be made so that they could operate properly, both when hot and when cold, and success in these modifications does not seem to have been achieved.

The most traumatic moment in the series of tests came one Sunday morning, when something catastrophic happened. A certain mystery surrounds what that 'something' really was. The usual story is that while the locomotive with its train was passing through Syston, a little to the north of Leicester, the whole sleeve assembly suddenly seized up, and it and the cylinders were destroyed; the line was blocked for the best part of the day until No 2299 could be towed back to Derby, and orders were then issued to discontinue trials forthwith. However, this version is corrected in a footnote to Kenneth Leech's account in the *Railway Gazette* of 2 November 1945, cited above. The Editor noted that he had been told on good authority that the engine was at a junction *south* of

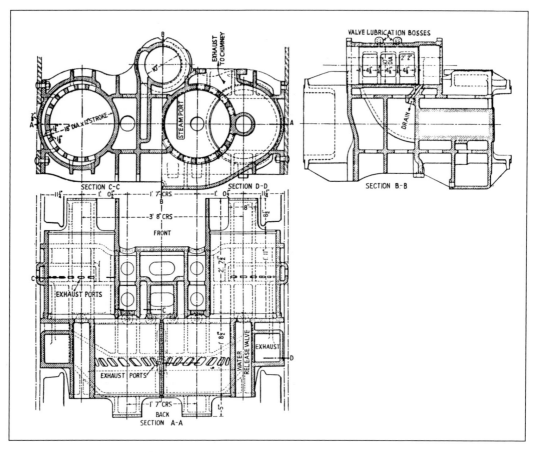

Leicester when its driving wheels bound while traversing a curve and brought it to a standstill. Steam then began to escape through the valves, which were not steam-tight, into the exhaust. It was necessary for the locomotive and train to be taken back to Derby, and since it could not go under its own steam it had to be towed by a shunting engine. Trouble now began in earnest; the pistons, working to and fro without steam for nearly 30 miles, damaged the interiors of the cylinders. Repairs were effected, and further trials were made, but what with one thing and another the enthusiasm of the works authorities, never very great, evaporated, and eventually No 2299 was put in an out-of-the-way place, covered up and left indefinitely. There was nothing Paget could do; he had run out of money and had had to agree to the 'limited testing only' condition.

Both accounts sound circumstantial, and perhaps both, or something like them, happened. If the latter event preceded the former, Paget's creation, like the world in T.S. Eliot's poem, came to an end 'not with a bang but a whimper'.

Sections across one of the two cylinder-and-valve castings in the Paget locomotive. (The Railway Gazette)

Paget himself, after Deeley's retirement in 1909, had every hope of succeeding him as Locomotive Superintendent. Had that been the case, no doubt No 2299 would have been brought out from beneath its coverings and worked upon until all the snags had been removed. But after the abrasive Mr Deeley, the board wanted a milder character and selected Henry Fowler, their Gas Engineer, who was not really a locomotive man at all. (On one occasion, long after his promotion, and in LMS days, when discussing with his Works Superintendent some modifications to the Walschaerts valve gear of a 2–6–4 tank locomotive, he admitted, 'Quite honestly, I don't understand the thing.') Paget was sent on an official investigative visit to the United States and then brought back to be appointed General Superintendent of the whole Midland Railway system. His energies were then expended on a complete reorganization of its traffic arrangements. Meanwhile, his rejected brain-child slumbered quietly under wraps in the paint shop at Derby.

The First World War broke out, and Paget volunteered for service. He went out to France early in 1915 to command the Railway Operating Division, Royal Engineers, and for more than three and a half years lived with his staff on a train which continually moved about as military exigencies required. He was accustomed to keep himself fit each morning by running the length of his 16-coach train and back before breakfast, in his pyjamas. When he eventually found himself in command of some 25,000 men he could have been raised to the rank of General had he so wished, but that would have meant removing himself to GHQ instead of remaining with his train and being on the spot when required, so he chose to remain a Lieutenant-Colonel. Once the War had ended he did not return to the Midland, but instead accepted the post of General Manager in a large engineering firm. He died in 1936 at the comparatively early age of 62. No 2299 had pre-deceased him by over 20 years, having been broken up at Derby as soon as its creator was safely out of the way in France. It was a victim of conventional thinking, short-sightedness, and perhaps also of envy.

It is not easy to evaluate Paget's locomotive. Some of its special features, such as the largely brick firebox, the rotary sleeve valves and the short-stroke trunk cylinders were not tried again in any British engine, except that O.V.S. Bulleid, when designing his ill-fated 'Leader' Class of general-purpose engines, used sleeve valves and a firebox with built-up brick sides. (The 'Leader' is described below, in Chapter 19). No 2299's speed capacity when hauling a full load (presumably some 300 tons) on level track was for its time quite an astonishing feat. It was thought pretty good going then for a locomotive with such a train to maintain 70 miles an hour on the flat; Paget's engine beat that by some 12 miles an hour — and with wheels only 5 ft 4 in diameter. One feels doubtful about those two fire doors. The driver and fireman would have had to spend a lot of time avoiding one another on the footplate. The locomotive was said to have run with remarkable smoothness, probably because its reciprocating parts were so few and because of its excellent balance. It had the advantage of disposing of its exhaust steam through separate orifices, so that the admission ports were not used for steam going in both directions — something whose avoidance was later sought when the 'Uniflow' locomotives of the North Eastern Railway were designed, as described below in Chapter 14. The slightly ungainly appearance could no doubt have been tidied up in subsequent production models.

As to the troublesome rotary valves, their fault seems to have been that they were made partly of bronze and partly of steel. The extent of differential expansion could probably have been lessened and perhaps eliminated when the right pair of metals had been discovered. Kenneth Leech, who had been one of Paget's subordinate officers in France during 1915–1918, had on one occasion managed to engage his Chief in a long conversation about the engine. At this time Paget probably did not know that it had been scrapped during his absence and was wondering how it could be made to work satisfactorily. Writing in the issue of the *Railway Gazette* mentioned at the beginning of this chapter, Leech says:

'Paget seemed more concerned at the time to hear my views of the best metals to use for the liners and valves, and I remember that my suggestion was to use cast iron for both parts and eliminate the differential expansion. In the light of nearly 25 years' more engineering experience .... I doubt whether anything except a radical re-design of the rotary valve would be satisfactory. A possible solution would be to use 2, 3 or 4 segmental valves instead of one C-valve[1], and rotate them at half engine speed, or slower as required, thus giving the lubrication a better chance and further helping things by the slow speed rotation. Nevertheless, especially with superheated steam, I should want to make a lot of tests before committing myself to a production design.

'But the valve gear, though important, was not a fundamental point of the design. The cylinders might have been modified to use four piston valves, one for each cylinder, either cam-operated or actuated by an ordinary valve gear. The cheap and simple boiler and the perfectly balanced free-running engine would have remained, and the development of the British locomotive might have taken a different course thereafter — but I was forgetting the Derby diehards.'

1 So-called because the liner was not quite a complete circle in section, but split lengthways, so that it looked like a letter C when seen edgeways-on, with the two arms nearly but not quite meeting. This was an attempt to allow it to expand when hot without seizing up — but it did not succeed.

13

Churchward's solitary 'Pacific'

Although it included no highly unusual features, the great engine which emerged from Swindon works in February 1908 was a novelty by its very size. It was longer and heavier than any contemporary locomotive in Great Britain, and had the longest boiler — almost 23 feet between tube-plates — of any ever to be built there. On its first appearance it created quite a stir. Charles Rous-Marten said it left him gasping with sheer amazement. One wondered then what was in the designer's mind when he built it. One is still wondering.

George Jackson Churchward was arguably the most important locomotive superintendent ever to have held that office in the days of steam, because of the influence he exerted over others, partly because they took his ideas with them when appointed to similar positions on other lines, and partly because, being already in positions of eminence on other lines, they saw what he was doing and were impressed. He was not a genius, always bubbling over with new notions, brilliant or bizarre, but a careful and methodical man who kept his eyes continually open to see what other railways were doing, whether in this country or abroad then asked himself what he could learn. The express engines he constructed were noted for their capability and efficiency. He was the last man to let himself be dominated by a whim, or to do anything on the spur of the moment. Nevertheless his largest creation, though not a failure, was not so successful as to warrant multiplication of the prototype. It was a decade and a half before its time, and when at last it vanished from the railway scene after 16 years of service, in 1924 Gresley's first 4–6–2s were just beginning to emerge from Doncaster. Churchward was said to be upset at its demise (he had now retired) and the Great Western Railway had certainly lost a cherished flag-bearer which had been given pride of place in the company's publicity ever since it was built. No other 'Pacific' ever came out of Swindon works.

Churchward was a Devonshire man. While as keen on sport as the average boy during his schooldays, he also showed a great interest in mathematics and in things mechanical, so that it was natural for him to become apprenticed at a railway works at the age of 16, first on the South Devon Railway at Newton Abbot, and later, after the Great Western absorbed that undertaking, at Swindon. Hard work and intelligence commended him to the Locomotive Superintendent, William Dean, and in his later thirties he became the latter's Chief Assistant. When that brilliant but somewhat wayward man began to show signs of mental failure before he was due to retire, Churchward was allowed almost imperceptibly to slip into his place, behaving towards Dean with the utmost tact and courtesy but nevertheless firmly taking up the reins. In the summer of 1902 he officially succeeded Dean. He had already adumbrated within his mind a general pattern of locomotive practice which he now began to follow out at Swindon. It was a product not only of his own individual thought but also of keen observation of both Continental and American practice. The end product was the typical Great Western locomotive, domeless, taper-boilered, with a Belpaire firebox, using high-pressure steam and tailored to run on the South Wales coal which his company always used — an engine which could be recognized anywhere. The trend he began was continued by his successors, Collett and Hawksworth, who carried on where he left off; the 'Granges', 'Manors' and 'Counties' of the Great Western's last days had the characteristic family likeness which had first shown itself in the company's first 4-6-0 express engine, No 100 *William Dean*, which had come out of Swindon 40 years earlier. Later railway engineers reverenced Churchward as the Grand Old Man who had gone on from strength to strength, never putting a foot wrong. However, no one is quite perfect, and eyebrows still rise when his great masterpiece is considered. Was *The Great Bear*, so to speak, also a Green Elephant?

At the time when he began to meditate its construction, no 'Pacific' had ever been built to run on British rails. He had been giving close attention, however, to what was happening in France and had, as is well known, imported three French-built four-cylinder compound 'Atlantics'

Churchward's 'Pacific', No 111 The Great Bear, as first built, with the forward steps up to the running plate which had to be removed since they fouled the platforms. (NRM)

to give their system of compounding a fair trial on Great Western metals and to see how they compared with his own non-compound engines. The line which sold him the last two compounds shortly afterwards built the first French 'Pacific', and this must have attracted his attention. A 'Pacific' could, of course, not only carry a larger boiler than an 'Atlantic', but also accommodate a wide firebox over its rear trailing wheels. As early as 1903, at a meeting of the Institution of Civil Engineers, after a paper had been read on 'American Locomotive Practice', he opened the discussion by saying:

'Probably, to English locomotive engineers, the part of the paper which deals with boilers is the most interesting; especially the reasonably wide firebox which the author has described. An express engine with a similar box has just been put on the Great Northern Railway by Mr Ivatt, and I trust it will have a good trial in England. I think English locomotive engineers are within measurable distance of adopting it, and I am sorry that the French "Atlantic" engine, which is to be put on the Great Western Railway, is not fitted with it — but I am taking this engine as it stands.'

Later, in February 1906, he himself read a paper to the Institution of Mechanical Engineers which began with the words 'The modern locomotive problem is still principally a question of boiler ....', and continued by saying that in the larger boilers that were then being built the circulation of water was generally poor. Space for such circulation ought especially to be provided near the rear tube-plate, which was nearer than any other part of the locomotive to the heat in the firebox. His own practice was now to increase the space between the inner and outer fireboxes (ie the water- and steam-filled space above and around the firebox proper) and to take the steam from above the firebox front. The flat-topped Belpaire furnace provided more room for steam bubbles to form and prevented foaming. It was not necessary to provide a steam dome. He had already made these changes in the engines he had built. He went on to display pictures of American fireboxes which were wide at the base, not narrower there than at mid-width as most British ones were, and had grate areas of up to 72 square feet — an enormous size compared with the largest he had himself so far used, 27 square feet. He evidently thought that extra grate size was a good thing if firemen could be trained to cope with it.

Within a year of his address, the Great Western Board of Directors had approved his suggestion of building a large-boilered 'Pacific' locomotive with a large firebox and wide grate, and made altogether more than £5,000 available to cover the project — 40 per cent more than his latest and very successful 'Star' 4-6-0s were costing. Detailed designing now went ahead. The machinery was to be little different from that in a 'Star', the coupled wheels being the same size, the cylinder stroke the same, the cylinder diameter only half an inch more and the valve gear,

The Great Bear, *before being rebuilt, with copper-capped chimney and without top feed, about to leave Paddington on a train for Bristol.* (LCGB)

Walschaerts', similarly placed inside the frames and operating the valves in the outside cylinders though rocking bars. With the same boiler pressure of 225 lbs per square inch, that made the 4-6-2 only a little more powerful in terms of maximum tractive effort than the earlier engines. The boiler, however, was very much larger, both in length and width; whereas that of the 'Star' was just over 15 feet long and tapered from 5 ft 3 in at the back to 4 ft 9 in at the front, the corresponding dimensions in *The Great Bear* were almost 23 feet and 6 feet tapering to 5 ft 6 in. In fact, it had twice the former's capacity.

Had Churchward wished he could have added another half-inch to the cylinder diameter by reducing the width of the tyres of the front bogie wheels by that amount; this would not have made them narrower than on most other British lines. The extra half-inch would have increased the locomotive's maximum tractive effort by about 2,700 lbs and brought it over the 30,000 mark. However, he would not compromise when safety, as he thought, might be in question, and vetoed the suggestion. Clearly he was not trying to increase the tractive effort, but wanted to provide a larger reserve of power during actual running. If the firebox could produce the heat needed to boil the extra water to provide the extra steam, the engine ought to be able to tackle heavier loads than the 'Stars' and, in unfavourable circumstances such as strong side winds or when climbing heavy gradients, should be able to put out the extra force without mortgaging its capacity to produce steam. To this huge boiler Churchward added a superheater, but one of only moderate size; he did not think it was necessary to do more than dry the steam and eliminate condensation in the cylinders.

Three other differences from his usual practice need noting. Though the engine did not need a larger tender he nevertheless gave it a longer one, which ran on two four-wheel bogies. He was sensitive to the appearance of his engines and evidently felt that a tender such as was supplied to the 'Stars' would look out of proportion. It held no more than 3,500 gallons of water, though this would scarcely matter on a route well supplied with water-troughs. The cab, too, was on the small side and did look rather disproportionate, but he extended the roof backwards to cover the tender fallplate. This gave the crew better shelter, but they were not used to being so shut in above; on one occasion a fireman got one of the fire-irons stuck between the footplate and the roof, and it took three men to shift it. After that the roof was made slightly shorter. The trailing axle beneath the firebox was also unusual. It had radial guides and inside springing, somewhat resembling the type invented by F.W.Webb, the wheel-axle running through a tube which was curved backwards and could move slightly from one side to the other within a similarly curved support. This device was always giving trouble, as it turned out. Cinders and ashes from the firegrate worked their way into the bearings and made them run hot.

Since the firegrate was half as large again as that of a 'Star', skilful firing was necessary and firemen had to discover the right technique. In the words of O.S. Nock (*The GWR Stars, Castles and Kings*, pp 82–83):

'The reputation that the engine earned at first for being an indifferent steamer was almost certainly due to the difficulty firemen experienced in feeding a grate that was so unlike those already in use on the Great Western Railway. This has occurred time and again with new locomotive designs, when engineers from the drawing office have had to ride the locomotives for weeks on end, fire themselves and find by hard experience the correct technique to use. One has known firemen almost break their hearts, and their backs (!), shovelling for dear life, when a much simpler and less fatiguing method would have produced far better results. This was certainly the case on the first Stanier 'Pacifics' on the LMSR, the boiler proportions of which have many points of similarity to those on *The Great Bear*. In later years the engine steamed well. I came to know some of the men that worked regularly on her, and they had nothing but praise for her general working and beautiful riding.'

The engine had its first trial trip on 4 February 1908 and a few minor problems were then ironed out. On the official photograph it is shown with steps to the running plate just ahead of the outside cylinders; however, when it first entered Paddington one of them fouled a platform, so they were removed from both sides. All pictures of the engine when at the head of a train show them absent.

The question now arose: on which trains should *The Great Bear* run?

As James Holden had found on the Great Eastern when he had put his own monster out, the Civil Engineer was the natural enemy of big engines. On the Great Western the latter official had insisted that only one route could safely accept the new 'Pacific' — the main line between Paddington and Bristol. This limitation nevertheless gave enough scope for using the engine profitably during the immediate future; the haulage of heavy expresses along a largely level or near level track, day in and day out in all conditions of wind and weather, would have enabled it to be established whether the locomotive was kind or cruel to the track it ran on. However, internal railway politics made it inadvisable just then to clash with the Civil Engineer's department. When the engine first appeared a serious dispute was developing between Sir James Inglis, the General Manager of the Company, and many of his chief officials over some organizational changes he was proposing to make; the latter, Churchward among them, were strenuously resisting their introduction. In such a situation it was important not to put a foot wrong, so Churchward exercised caution, and no one ever really found out whether *The Great Bear* was hard on the track or not. One consideration which exercised the Civil Engineer was the weak state of many of the underbridges on the system. A start had been made at strengthening

The Great Bear, *before rebuilding, waiting to back on to a train at Paddington. Note the photographer's shadow!*(NRM)

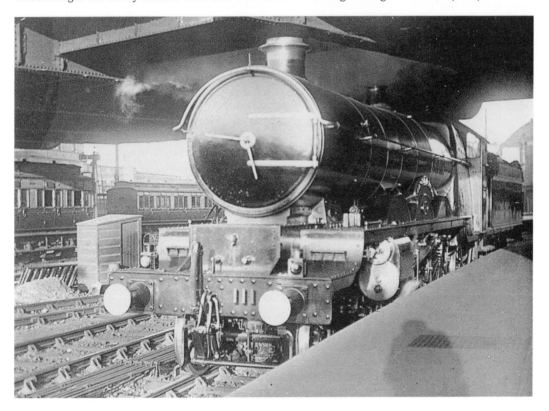

The Great Bear, in its rebuilt state, with cast-iron chimney and top feed apparatus, leaving Paddington at the head of an express train. (NRM)

them but the process had not gone very far. So only once or twice did the engine stray from its allotted route.

During the first five years of its existence it worked regularly on expresses between London and Bristol, and was most frequently to be seen on the evening dining-car train from Paddington to the West Country which travelled by way of Bristol and took the level two hours to reach Bath, slipping a coach at Chippenham. By the eve of the First World War it was speeded up to leave 10 minutes later, and only took 112 minutes to reach Bath, at an average speed of 57¼ miles an hour. O.S.Nock, in the book quoted above, mentions a run behind it, timed by a friend of his, in which a moderate load of 310 tons was taken as far as Chippenham, and 25 tons less from there to Bath, which was reached in a minute and a half over schedule, with a signal check before Reading and another on the approach to Bath, the net time being about 110 minutes; but for the concluding check, time would have been kept. There were no fireworks; most of the way between Steventon and Swindon, on faintly rising grades, the speed was well under the mile-a-minute rate, and the maximum before Chippenham was probably not much over 70. A 'Saint' could have done as well. But the train was on time nearly all the way so there was no point in going faster. Perhaps better times were made on other occasions, or much heavier loads were worked to time, but one does not know; train timers were few in those days. Rous-Marten would no doubt have gone out of his way to observe what the engine could do, and no doubt the footplatemen would have obliged him by showing its paces. Alas, he died in April 1908, and his successors who continued his regular articles in *The Railway Magazine* were not sufficiently curious to see whether the new giant could exercise a giant's strength.

Towards the end of 1913 *The Great Bear* re-entered Swindon works and some modifications were made. Top feed apparatus was now being fitted to all Great Western engines, and this was installed in the 4-6-2; feed water, instead of being injected into the boiler through clack-boxes fairly low down, was taken up pipes which encircled the outer cladding to reach the brass safety-valve cover and entered the boiler there, dropping over plates to which impurities in the water tended to adhere and which could easily be removed for cleaning. A new superheater was also fitted, with slightly reduced superheating surface. A cast-iron chimney replaced the original copper-capped one. The cab was given a new steel roof. Alterations were made to the springing of the wheels. Apart from the top feed pipes and the new chimney, the external appearance was much the same as before.

Then came the First World War, and interest shifted away from the improvement of locomotives and their performance until the fighting was over. By now Churchward was near his retirement, and his mind was occupied with other matters, such as fitting his other engines with larger boilers. *The Great Bear*, while still officially the company's flagship, proudly illustrated and described in publicity material, was never given any of the principal expresses to run. A common turn for it, when it was not hauling freight trains, was the semi-fast 10.45 am to Cheltenham, which it hauled as far as Swindon, taking almost two hours to cover the 77¼ miles, with three intermediate stops, a sorry assignment for a heavyweight champion. Soon after the 1923 groupings its place as flagship was taken by the 4-6-0 *Caerphilly Castle*, and after the building of more 'Castles' it was dismantled. Officially it was itself rebuilt as a 'Castle', but very little of the original was used when *Viscount Churchill* appeared except the wheels and the numberplate, the front end of the main frames and the cylinders.

14

Two 'Uniflow' locomotives on the North Eastern Railway

The steam locomotive never has been a thermally efficient way of converting heat from fossil fuel into mechanical energy, and probably it never could be. It has, however, the advantage of depending on two things which the United Kingdom possesses in abundance — water and coal. The water costs almost nothing (though against that has to be set the cost of cleaning boiler and tubes from deposited scale) and the coal has been relatively cheap throughout most of our recent history (sometimes because of disgraceful reasons, such as the use of cheap labour by women and children required to work underground). Still, over and above the cost of extracting it from the ground there had to be added the expense of transporting it to places where it could be conveniently transferred to the tenders or bunkers of locomotives. It *did* cost the railway companies money, so economy in its use was something to be aimed at. Hence the experiments in compounding already mentioned, and other experiments to be described in subsequent chapters.

The lumps of coal which the fireman shovelled into the firebox never had more than a small percentage of their potential heat energy converted into drawbar-pull. However well the heated parts might be lagged, some heat escaped by radiation from them. Gases of combustion passed through the boiler tubes to be exhausted through the chimney still hot enough to throw sparks unless the engine was being very easily worked. The steam which came from the blast pipe was still hot steam, only condensing when it reached the atmosphere. Even when it was at work in the cylinders it had to act against the friction of moving parts, which oiling could lessen but not remove, and against air resistance as the locomotive moved forward, which increased very rapidly when high speeds were attained. If one-twelfth of the energy latent in the coal could be made available for pulling the train the engine was doing well.

Locomotive engineers had therefore always given careful attention to any likely means of reducing loss of heat. A certain amount of this took place within the cylinder valves and the cylinders. In the conventional type of double-acting cylinder there were inlet ports for steam from the boiler which were alternately opened and closed by the steam valves, and at either end of the interior of the cylinder there were also 'clearance space surfaces' which the piston at the end of its stroke approached but did not quite meet. When hot steam under high pressure entered from the boiler, in the course of doing its work against the reciprocating piston face it lost some of its heat, and so slightly cooled both the ports themselves and the surface of the adjacent clearance space when the later backward thrust of the piston on the return stroke forced it out again by the same route. The cooling at any one expulsion, and the re-heating when the next packet of steam took its place, were of course slight, but they happened several times a second when the engine was travelling fast, so the total heat loss in a given short space of time would in sum be quite considerable. Furthermore, when live steam entered the cylinder and impinged on the cooled clearance space surfaces, condensation could occur and cause damage.

However, if it were possible to expel the used steam through vents other than the admission ports, both the cooling effects and the tendency to condensation could be avoided. In the Paget locomotive, as was seen above in Chapter 12, this was achieved; all the steam entering one of his eight trunk cylinders left it at the end of each stroke through a ring of holes momentarily uncovered by the piston, so that there was no cooling at or near the inlet ports. To get the same result with double-acting cylinders, where should such orifices be? Professor Stumpf, of Charlottenburg Technical College, Berlin, addressed himself to this question in 1909 and came up with an answer. The steam exit ports, he said, should be round the circumference and in the middle of a double-acting cylinder, the interior of the latter being twice as long as its stroke, so that a very long piston would uncover them at the end of each stroke either way. The steam, entering the cylinder at either end alternately, would always leave through the same exit ports through which the flow would always be in the same direction, outward towards the blast pipe (hence the term 'Uniflow').

To understand the events in a Uniflow cylinder it will help to imagine them. At the beginning of stroke, when steam is admitted (usually when the piston has not quite reached the end wall, so that a cushioning is given between it and the wall), the piston face is pressed back with maximum force, which is needed to overcome the inertia in a moving system which for a split second has become still. Once the steam has been cut off, that which is already within the cylinder expands and continues to push the piston backwards until it reaches the end of the stroke, with lessening pressure as it expands. However, the reciprocating piston and the parts attached to it have now gathered a momentum which to some extent makes up for the lessening pressure. So far what has happened is the same in all steam cylinders, in the Uniflow, when 90 per cent of the stroke has been completed, the

The South Eastern Railway's 2-2-2 Man of Kent, *which had double-length 'Uniflow' cylinders, though they were not yet so named.*

exhaust orifices are uncovered and for a very short while the imprisoned steam rushes out past the piston edge and escapes towards the blast pipe; the time when it can do so is short, but seeing there are many exit ports, sufficient.

The return stroke then begins, with the events at the other end of the cylinder matching those which have already occurred at the front end. The pressure in its forward part has now been lowered to that of the atmosphere, and presses back only to a slight extent because it cannot escape at once; thus it hinders, but only very slightly, the push of the returning piston, which eventually reaches the end of its stroke, and the active steam behind it exhausts through the exit ports as the previous package of steam has done. The cycle is then repeated. The Uniflow system thus has the advantage that cooled steam does not lower the temperature at and around the inlet ports, that there is no forcing of exhaust steam through narrow passages, and condensation will not occur.

When the cut-off is a long one, however, and not all the steam in the cylinder has time to escape from the central ring of exhaust ports, what then? When Sir Vincent Raven and his design team at Darlington, having the construction of a Uniflow locomotive in mind, considered this, they came up with a simple answer. If the engine were being worked on a long cut-off (which would not happen very often, but would necessarily *have* to happen when the train was being started from rest), the valve events would have to provide that some steam could escape through the inlet ports as the piston pressed the residue back. The engine which emerged from Darlington works early in 1913, built in this way, could therefore be termed a 'semi-Uniflow' type, though in practice the full uni-directional flow of exhaust steam was achieved once the engine was linked up to a fairly short cut-off.

The engineers at Darlington were not the first to build this kind of locomotive. In the early days of the South Eastern Railway, one of its engines, a 2–2–2 with 6 ft drivers named *Man of Kent*, was rebuilt in 1849 with a new pair of cylinders twice as long as the previous ones, 36 instead of 18 inches, their extra lengths projecting forwards from the smokebox base. A built-up piston-head 17 inches long traversed each one. At the mid-point of the cylinder barrel was an exhaust port extending half-way round the inner circumference, which the long piston uncovered at the end of each stroke in either direction. Most of the steam escaped through this port; what was left was expelled through the port by which it had entered and then taken to the blast pipe along a copper pipe which emerged from beneath the running plate, bent round to come upwards through it, and then turned back to enter the smokebox. It can be clearly seen in the accompanying drawing. Exactly who was responsible for the design of this engine, using an idea essentially the same as Stumpf was later to come up with, is not known, nor do we know what he was trying to achieve, though it seems likely he had the same end in view. However, the locomotive did not apparently work satisfactorily since it was rebuilt with conventional cylinders three years later.

Raven, who had succeeded Wilson Worsdell as Chief Mechanical Engineer on the North Eastern after the latter's retirement, modified the last 'S' Class 4–6–0 mixed traffic locomotive to be built at Darlington (where locomotives were now being constructed instead of at Gateshead) by giving it two Uniflow cylinders with the modification already mentioned. To do this, a considerable rearrangement of parts had been necessary at the leading end. Two enormous cylinders on the

A superb official photograph of the North Eastern Railway's 'Uniflow' 4-6-0 No 825, shown in photographic grey before it received the railway's livery and entered service. The cylinders look almost aggressive. (NRM)

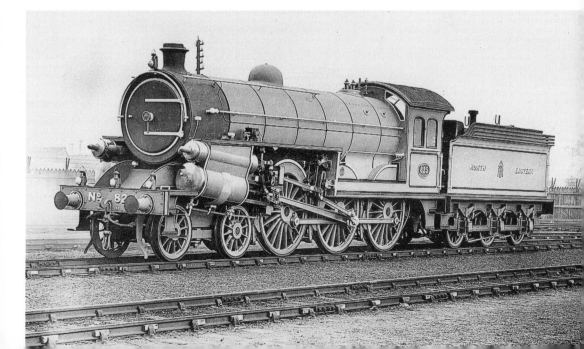

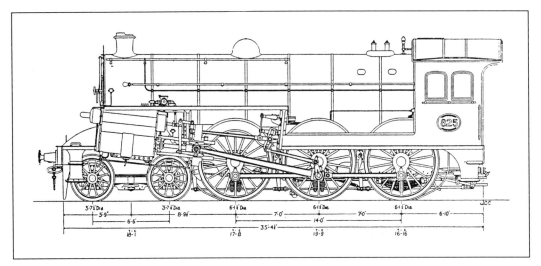

Above *A dimensioned side view of No 825. (The Engineer)*

Right *Front view of the NER 'Uniflow' 4-6-0 No 825. (NRM)*

outside of the front end now projected forwards and upwards like a pair of missile-launchers, and it must be confessed that the result was anything but beautiful. Piston valves admitted steam at either end, which eventually for the most part was exhausted through the ring of ports centrally placed around each cylinder barrel — and, as mentioned above, through the inlet ports as well when the engine was not linked up. It was necessary to raise the running plate on either side over each cylinder by some three feet in order to make room not only for the great bulk of the latter but also for the valve gear, now placed outside the frames. Accordingly an extra hand-rail was fixed on each side of the boiler quite near the chimney and dome.

The total effect was distinctly untidy, and one imagines that if the type had been multiplied some attempt would have been made to clean up the external appearance. However, no more 4-6-0s emerged from Darlington to match it. Could it be said that handsome was as handsome did? We do not know, for no detailed records of its performance were released, and no logs by train-timers appear to be extant. When releasing details of it to *The Engineer*, Raven had said that it had 'given satisfaction', and that he was keeping it under observation and giving it

'...special work to find out what it can do ... During the early part of this month the engine was employed on the 10.28 am express passenger train from Newcastle to York, and on the 1.52 pm Scotch express back from York. The weight of the 10.28 am train varied from 283 to 321 tons, and the average speed maintained was 51.7 miles an hour. The weight of the 1.52 pm train ranged from 314 to 363 tons and the average speed was 51.1 miles per hour.

Longitudinal and transverse sections of No 825's left-hand cylinder, showing the complete ring of exit ports for the exhaust steam. (The Engineer)

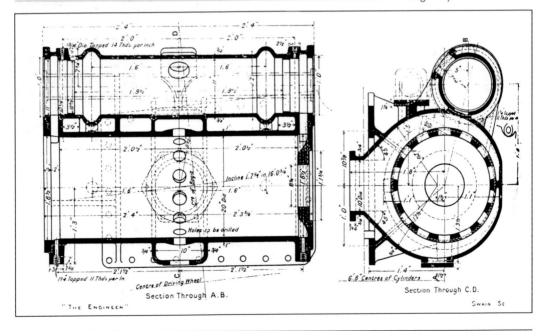

Section Through A.B.

Section Through C.D.

Top *No 825 resting between duties at Heaton shed, Newcastle, in May 1920. (LCGB)*

Above *No 2212, the NER 'Atlantic' built with three 'Uniflow' cylinders, which despite their size are completely hidden from view. (NRM)*

These figures do not sound very impressive, corresponding as they do with times between Newcastle and York, and in the reverse direction, of 93 and 94 minutes respectively, though if the latter had been made with 363 tons, which would have been more if one were to count in the passenger and luggage complement, that was not bad going. Had *net* times been given, one could have assessed the performance better.

In fact, No 825 did not last long in its original state. In March 1924 it was rebuilt with normal cylinders and valves to match its fellows. However, Raven seems to have been sufficiently encouraged by its performance to make the further experiment, in 1919, of building one of his 'Z' Class 'Atlantics' on the Uniflow system, this time with three cylinders which, marvellous to relate, he managed to keep out of sight, though two of them were outside the frames. No 2212 was the guinea pig on this occasion. The casting for all three cylinders was made in one block, a most impressive piece of foundry work. The upward tilt of the cylinders was much slighter than in No 825, and box casings covered the outside cylinders so neatly that one had to look twice to realize that this was in fact the Uniflow 'Atlantic'. This time the valve gear was kept within the frames. The bogie front wheels had to be spaced further apart and made six inches smaller in diameter than in the other 'Z' Atlantics', to allow room for the enlarged cylinders. The whole engine was two and a half tons heavier than its non-Uniflow fellows, the additional weight resting almost entirely on the leading bogie.

Little is known of how it performed on the road. According to Cecil J. Allen, in his book *British Atlantic Locomotives* it achieved 'no great success'. K. Hoole, on the other hand, in his book *North Eastern Atlantics*, says that it was 'a favourite for the Pullman turns [from Newcastle] to Leeds Central, via Northallerton, Ripon and Harrogate' — a road which between Harrogate and Leeds has some very stiff gradients which could be quite trying. The 'Queen of Scots' Pullman was not a heavy proposition — seven vehicles weighing some 280 tons were a usual load between Edinburgh and Leeds — but it *was* a prestige train,

Front view of No 2212, showing no sign of the presence of the three enormous cylinders behind the valances just to the rear of the buffers. (NRM)

The huge single casting containing the three 'Uniflow' cylinders and valves for NER 'Atlantic' No 2212.

so the Uniflow 'Atlantic' must at least have been reliable or it would not have been selected for the job. In 1934 it went to Darlington for overhaul after 16 years in its original condition, and only then was it decided to modify it and use it for a second experiment, giving it new cylinders of the usual kind, but with Lentz poppet valves. In its reconstructed form it lasted until October 1945.

One has to assume that whatever economies the Uniflow locomotives may have achieved must have been too small to warrant the types being multiplied. They had two inescapable disadvantages to set against their theoretical advantages — extra weight and heavier reciprocating masses — and, as has been seen already, the latter weighed against the continuance of the Nesbit system of compounding. When the whole tendency of locomotive design is in a particular direction, anything purporting to be better has to be a great deal better in order to oust its predecessors and justify all the upheavals that would be necessary in works which were geared to the old order of things.

15

Maunsell's 'K' Class tank locomotives

Was it possible for a railway company successfully to use tank locomotives on express trains? The London, Brighton & South Coast Railway began doing so as early as 1909, when Class 'L3' tank engines were rostered to haul London-Brighton expresses, notably the 60-minute 'Southern Belle' Pullman. D. Marsh, the Locomotive Superintendent, who had designed these engines, also built two 4–6–2s for express work just before his retirement; following his example, his successor, L. Billinton, went one pair of wheels better and constructed seven 4–6–4s, the last of which appeared just before his company was merged into the Southern Railway. These seven engines had been designed to run from Victoria to Portsmouth, the longest through run possible on the Brighton line, without having to take water *en route*; side tanks holding 2,000 gallons were considered large enough for this. When the first one came out in 1914 it suffered a few teething troubles, in particular a tendency to roll when the tanks were half filled with water. The fault was corrected, but it was a pointer towards the future.

The first question suggests another: could a fairly small company run its expresses *exclusively* with tank locomotives? Neither Marsh nor Billinton seems to have thought of doing this, since between them they only built nine six-coupled tank locomotives in the Brighton line's last 15 years as an independent company. On the neighbouring South Eastern & Chatham Railway, however, this was the intention of R.E.L. Maunsell, who succeeded H. Wainwright as Locomotive Superintendent in 1913, and he built an engine to make it possible. Circumstances then frustrated his design.

Maunsell was an Irishman who had been in charge at Inchicore works on the Great Southern & Western Railway for two years before coming to Ashford. He came there in unusual circumstances. Wainwright was nowhere near retiring age — he was not yet 50 — but heart trouble and the tragedy of a failed marriage to a spendthrift wife who eventually deserted him had undermined his energies, and by 1912 he was not the man he had been. He was at odds with his Directors over what appeared to them to be inefficiency at Ashford works, where they thought he delegated too much responsibility, and he was eventually induced to resign. Maunsell, when he succeeded him early in 1913, was told that he was expected to rule his department firmly, and to encourage him he was given a salary considerably larger than Wainwright had received.

The latter had largely left the designing of new locomotives to his Chief Draughtsman, Robert Surtees, but Maunsell had definite ideas of his own. He had been impressed by Churchward's work on the Great Western, especially by his policy of standardization, and he resolved to put some of the Swindon ideas into practice. He recruited a number of young and able railway engineers from other lines to replace most of Wainwright's senior staff, some of whom were near retirement in any case. With the admixture of new blood and tactful handling of some of the old guard who still remained, by the summer of 1914 he was set to make the South Eastern & Chatham a different sort of line and Ashford works a different sort of place. Then came the First World War, which put everything else in the shade and resulted, indirectly, in the merging of his railway into a larger group.

During the war years, when he was not engaged in work for the Government as Chief Mechanical Engineer to the Railway Executive Committee, which co-ordinated the efforts of all the private railway companies in the national interest, Maunsell found time to anticipate the end of hostilities and consider the peace-time needs of his company, when its primary task would cease to be the carrying of men and munitions to the Western Front. The South Eastern & Chatham Railway fulfilled three main tasks. It ran an extensive commuter traffic, not yet with the benefit of electrification, from North-east Kent to London; it linked the capital with all parts of Kent and some parts of East Sussex, especially the holiday coast from Whitstable round to Bexhill, and it ran the boat trains for the Continent by way of Dover, Folkestone and (for a while) Sheerness. It was much more a passenger than a freight line. To run its expresses there were no really powerful locomotives. Wainwright's 'D' and 'E' Class 4-4-0s had coped well when the loads were light and the schedules easy, and at the end of his superintendency the latter had ordered 20 'L' Class 4-4-0s, with larger boilers and somewhat more powerful, but nowhere on the system was there a six-coupled passenger locomotive (though designs for one had been prepared). Yet more powerful engines were certainly going to be needed to haul the increasing loads. Boat trains, especially, which carried large amounts of heavy baggage as well as passengers, promised to be heavier than in the past. Some strengthening of the permanent way, and of underbridges, was also going to be necessary. This, of course, was not Maunsell's responsibility, though the state of the track limited what he could do. New locomotives were going to be needed to run with adequate speed and tackle the severe banks on the two main lines to Dover by way of Tonbridge and Chatham — banks which generally did not exceed 1 in 100 but were frequent and sometimes awkwardly situated. Any acceleration of services required a different kind of engine, both for mixed traffic and for express trains.

During the early war years what suggested itself to Maunsell was that there should be two basic six-coupled designs, both able to operate over the greater part of the company's system except between Tonbridge and Hastings, which because of unduly narrow tunnels would have to be worked by existing smaller engines. The six-couplers should be able to cope with the larger loads. One of the two designs was a 2–6–0 outside-cylindered tender engine with 5 ft 6 in driving wheels; the other was a 2–6–4 tank engine with the same boiler, cylinders, motion and front end arrangements. The 2–6–0 was for mixed traffic; the 2–6–4 (and here was the novelty) was to take over *all* the fast passenger traffic except for the boat trains, and its driving wheels were to be 6 ft wide.

Maunsell felt no anxiety about the adequacy of the 2–6–4's coal and water supplies. If Billinton's 4–6–4s could manage an 80 mile run without a refill, so should his new 2–6–4s, with tanks of equal capacity and all the advantages which came from adopting Swindon-type improvements. The longest express run on the South Eastern & Chatham was only 78 miles. As to the adequacy of 6 ft wheels for express work, what mattered more than racing along the level and downhill stretches was the ability to surmount steepish banks. More time would be lost by slow progress uphill than could be regained by hurrying downhill and along the level. Six feet would be enough — and when one considers the later feats of Stanier's 6-foot 'Black Fives' and Bulleid's 6 ft 2 in 'Pacifics' (which could touch 100 miles an hour when put to it) one must agree that Maunsell was right.

Design began on both types in 1914 and the prototypes appeared three years later. The 2–6–4, No 790, was the first of the two to emerge from Ashford; though drably apparelled in wartime grey, it was an impressive machine none the less. The South Eastern & Chatham's long 'inside cylinders only' tradition was now broken. Massive outside piston-valved cylinders with outside Walschaerts valve gear proclaimed the new order of things, as also did the tapered boiler, pressed to 200 lbs per square inch, and the backward-sloping Belpaire firebox. What looked like a steam dome was really a top-feed apparatus, as the pipes leading upwards on either side of the boiler showed. Steam collection took place at the highest point in the boiler, in accordance with Churchward's practice. Long tail-rods protruded from the fronts of the 19 in by 28 in cylinders (these were later found to be unnecessary and were removed). Tractive effort was 23,866 lbs, considerably more than that of the 'L' Class 4–4–0s. Here was the passenger locomotive of the future, able to cope with the expected increased loads, run like other tank engines equally well in either direction, and meant to displace existing passenger types as its numbers were multiplied.

When design on the 2–6–4 had started there was not yet any suspicion that the separate days of the South Eastern & Chatham Company were

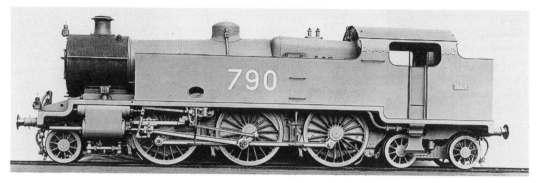

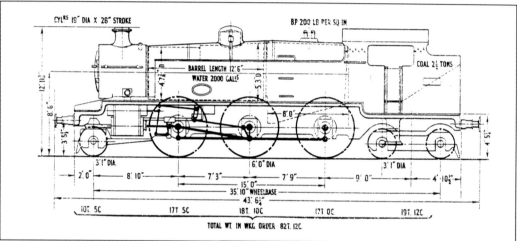

Top *R.E.L Maunsell's 2-6-4 express tank locomotive No 790 for the South Eastern & Chatham Railway, in wartime grey, after construction at Ashford in 1917. (NRM)*

Above *Dimensioned diagram of No 790. (Ian Allan)*

numbered, but towards the end of the war the intention of the Government to do something about the railways became known, the war having made obvious the advantages of a unified system. Maunsell was aware of this and possibly saw that his notion of a single type of express engine for his own company was going to be outmoded by the march of history. For the moment he built no more 2-6-4s but concentrated on the 2-6-0s, which had impressed the Railway Executive by their suitability for mixed traffic work. Indeed, as soon as the war ended, Woolwich Arsenal was given the job of producing a hundred of them, in the expectation that they would find immediate use all over a newly nationalized system.

However, the latter never came to pass. Other advice prevailed, and it was decided that the post-war pattern was to be four large groupings of existing companies, one of which would include the London & South Western, London, Brighton & South Coast and South Eastern & Chatham railways. As things turned out, Maunsell, being the youngest of the three Chief Mechanical Engineers on these lines, did well out of the change; he was chosen to hold that position on the newly formed

Southern Railway, and so exchanged his kingdom for an empire. The construction of the 2–6–0s went ahead, but for the moment the solitary 2–6–4 was to undergo tests to see whether it could do what it had been built to do. A little while before the ending of hostilities it was put on an afternoon express from Charing Cross to Folkestone Junction, which was to run non-stop over the 71 miles. The load was 310 tons empty, and probably 340 tons altogether. The schedule was a leisurely 102 minutes, but fireworks were not expected — the track was in no state for fast running — and the main interest lay in seeing whether the tanks held enough water. They did, but only just; another ten miles would have emptied them. The hint was taken and neither No 790 nor its fellows, after they were built, were asked to run non-stop further than to Ashford. Maunsell had obviously been too optimistic.

During 1925–1926, 19 sister engines to No 790 were built, as well as an additional three-cylinder engine which used a form of derived valve gear for the inside cylinder. As if to emphasize that these were pukka express locomotives, the Southern Railway Board decided to name all 20 after rivers which flowed through its territory.

How good were these engines? Or should one ask, how bad? Trials conducted in 1921, when multiplication of the design was being considered, did not show No 790 up in quite the expected favourable light. The 'L' Class engine against which it was tested, though only four-coupled, made the faster running with similarly weighted trains and did not burn more coal. This was quite unexpected. Then, once the 20 new engines had been completed, and they had been put on the road, another fault showed up. Complaints began to come in from drivers that they had a tendency to roll. The fault was partly in the engines, water surging about in their tanks and causing instability. It was also partly in the track. Weak spots had begun to develop in the latter because such heavy engines were passing over it at high speeds. Drivers tended, when they knew where these weak places were, to slow down when passing over them. Naturally, timekeeping suffered. One contributory reason for the lines in Kent not having a consistently good and firm track was that in the past, shingle, available in large quantities from Kentish beaches, had been placed on a bed of ash to support the rail sleepers. The rounded pebbles had no angles by which to grip one another and subsidences occurred here and there, so that 'soft patches' were formed. Over much of the system the shingle had been replaced by broken fragments of Kentish ragstone, but there were still unimproved patches here and there.

Very soon after the whole class had been put on the road, derailments began to occur, three happening on the secondary main line between Swanley and Ashford. Finally, on 24 August 1927 the 5.00 pm express from Cannon Street to Folkestone, Dover and East Kent, a prestige train with a Pullman car in its formation, suffered a serious accident. Headed by No 800 *River Cray*, it left the rails on a curve north of Sevenoaks when travelling at speed, and the coaches crashed into the side of a bridge. There were many fatal casualties. An outcry arose in the Press about the 'Rolling Rivers' and they were withdrawn from service. Tested on the London & North Eastern main line, they did not appear to be inherently unsteady; re-tested on the former London & South Western main line, however, they showed a tendency to sway when the track bed was less than perfect. If all the routes on which they had been meant to run could have had their 'soft spots' put right, they could have continued to be used, but the improvements would take a long while. They were already in progress, Meldon granite chips from Dartmoor replacing the shingle, but so far as the engines were concerned it was decided to rebuild them without tanks, attaching tenders instead, and this was done. 'King Arthurs' now took their places on the expresses to the Kent Coast, and a little later the 'Lord Nelsons' appeared on the boat trains. The rebuilt engines lost their names; they sometimes appeared on fast trains during periods of heavy seasonal traffic, but mostly they were used as maids-of-all-work.

Maunsell's intentions might have been fulfilled if the permanent way had been improved earlier, and if two or three sets of water troughs had been laid down. No doubt this was considered, but a glance at the gradient profiles shows that there were not many level stretches where this could have been conveniently done; on the old South Eastern line there was one a mile short of Ashford, and another lay between Gillingham and Rainham on the former London, Chatham & Dover line. Also, while picking up water at speed into a tender presented no great difficulties, it would have presented design problems when the water storage was at the engine's sides and not behind the footplate. As things were, of the four post-war groupings the Southern was the only one which had no troughs anywhere, and which accordingly even with large-tendered engines could never manage any really long non-stop runs, London to Bournemouth being the absolute limit.

'K' Class tank locomotive No 810 River Cray, Southern Railway, one of the batch built by Maunsell during the 'twenties and similar to No 790, hauling a stopping train. (This locomotive was involved in the fatal accident at Sevenoaks in August 1927.) (NRM)

16

Booster locomotives on the London & North Eastern Railway

Adhesion has always been a limiting factor in the effective use of a steam locomotive. However large a nominal tractive effort it may possess, however great its boiler's ability to produce steam, these things will avail nothing if the driving wheels do not get a firm grip on the rails. For this reason, as explained above in Chapter 9, the graceful single drivers built towards the end of the nineteenth century had to be withdrawn from main-line express services in the early years of the twentieth century as loadings increased. Even though steam sanding might permit them to start a heavy train, once the latter was in motion slipping would still continue and the pull on the drawbar would be to some extent lessened. So four-coupled engines took the place of the singles, and they in turn began to be supplanted by six-coupled engines, so that at the time of the groupings in 1923 the only companies which had none of the latter for use on express passenger trains were the Midland, the North British and the Great North of Scotland railways. The usual wheel arrangement favoured was the 4-6-0, with inside or outside cylinders or with three or four cylinders. With such a locomotive, up to 60 tons or so in weight could be placed on the driving wheels, so it was possible to increase tractive effort by enlarging cylinder capacity as long as the boiler could supply adequate steam. The most powerful express passenger locomotive on British rails at the end of 1922 was Gresley's 4-6-2 on the Great Northern Railway, with a tractive effort, at 85 per cent of boiler pressure, of 29,835 lbs.

However, on many British lines there were many 4-4-2s which had been built at some time during the pre-war years. Some were as large and weighty as many of the 4-6-0s, and some had very large boilers; many had also received superheating. Their trailing trucks each supported a great deal of weight, but this was not available for adhesion since their wheels were not cylinder-driven. Such locomotives, given a really heavy train to haul, might cope successfully if skilfully handled and if the rails were dry, but if the latter were wet, or greasy, or had fallen leaves adhering to their upper surfaces, severe slipping might begin. Not surprisingly, therefore, the 4–4–2 'Atlantic' type began to go out of fashion, no new ones being designed after the outbreak of the First World War. They had nevertheless plenty of life left in them at the time of the 1923 groupings; the question was, could anything be done to increase their haulage capacity without actually rebuilding them as 4–6–0s — which the Great Western actually did with its 15 British-built ones but which could not have been done easily with those on the Great Northern and London, Brighton & South Coast railways because of their wide fireboxes.

The United States led the way in answering this question. In 1919 the New York Central Railroad rebuilt one of its express engines, which had a trailing truck under the firebox and cab, by substituting for this truck one which had a 'booster' engine. (The term 'booster' was an American slang word which quickly passed into English usage; it would not be easy to find a suitably descriptive word, using only standard English, which was as short and snappy). The booster truck had a pair of cylinders installed which worked the axle through cranks and a system of gearing that could be engaged or disengaged by means of a lever in the cab. Steam was provided from the boiler and its entry to the cylinders was controlled by a separate regulator. So, when extra power was needed it could be given through what were in effect an extra pair of driving wheels.

In principle this device was similar to Archibald Sturrock's steam tender, already described in Chapter 4, but it was the weight at the rear end of the locomotive, not the weight of the loaded tender, which provided the extra adhesion.

It was evident that, if such a booster were being used, there would be a greater drain on the boiler steam, and it might be asked whether enough of the latter could be supplied. The answer would clearly have to be that the supply would be sufficient as long as the engine was moving slowly. In such a circumstance the locomotive's main cylinders would take steam only once or twice a second, while the boiler at the same time would be producing steam at a more or less constant rate. Up to a certain point, therefore, there would be steam to spare. Once the engine had got its load moving and was well under way, the booster would no longer be needed and could be disengaged and have its supply of steam cut off. When it had been cut out, the extra resistance in its reciprocating parts would also be cut out and the rear wheels would revert to their role of mere supporters of part of the weight of the engine. Supposing a really tough gradient was reached, it could then be cut in again by engaging the gears and opening the booster's steam regulator. The ideal line on which a booster might be used would be one which had occasional steep pitches, both at the starting point and subsequently.

Gresley became interested in the possibility of using boosters soon after his first twelve 'Pacifics' had come out. He had at his disposal a large number of 'Atlantics' which his predecessor had built, with large boilers and wide fireboxes; their cylinders were only 18 in by 24 in, and for their tractive capability they were all over-boilered. They were still relied on for much of the express work on the newly formed London & North Eastern Railway south of York and Leeds, as the new 'Pacifics' Gresley had built or was in process of building, together with the five that Raven had constructed for the North Eastern Railway just before the groupings, were by no means sufficient to cope with the whole of the East Coast express service. The 'Atlantics' were not yet 20 years old, and all had now been given superheaters to improve their performances; however, with such capacious boilers more could conceivably be got out of them. Enlarging their cylinders would have been one way of doing this; to raise their steam pressure, another. Nevertheless, they would still each only have the adhesion of a four-coupled locomotive. The fitting of a booster would increase adhesion as well as power when both were needed, so he ordered one from the Franklin Supply Company of New York and fitted it to 'Atlantic' No 4419 (in the new LNER numbering).

The steam pipes to the booster cylinders were visible externally; they emerged from behind and beneath the smokebox, extended backwards on either side of the engine above the running plate, passed through the lower cab front and then turned downwards to feed the booster cylinders, which were under the footplate and drove forwards on to the carrying wheels. In order to accommodate the booster, the frames were somewhat lengthened and the cab was enlarged backwards so that it resembled that of a 'Pacific'. A Westinghouse pump on the right-hand side of the smokebox supplied compressed air to operate the device

Ivatt 'Atlantic' No 4419, as rebuilt by H.N. Gresley with booster apparatus. (NRM)

which brought the booster gear wheels into engagement by pressing air into a cylinder whose piston went downwards against the force of a spring which normally kept the gears disengaged. Steam could then be admitted into the booster cylinders. The reciprocating and revolving parts of the booster engine were lubricated by being immersed in an oil bath. It was obligatory upon the driver never to cut the booster in if the speed of the locomotive exceeded 10 miles an hour, and to cut it out as soon as 21 miles an hour was attained. No provision was made for the booster to work in reverse.

A first test of the locomotive so modified was made on 29 July 1924, to see whether the engine could work a train as heavy as any likely ever to leave King's Cross station, and also to discover whether it could re-start at any point on the line — which in practice meant whether it could re-start on the 1 in 107 which begins almost at the platform end at King's Cross. A rake of coaches weighing 535 tons was to be hauled from the terminus as far as Hatfield. A log of the journey is appended. It will be seen that at the start, the use of the booster reduced the boiler pressure a little; that the second start, at Copenhagen signal box, on the most difficult gradient of the whole line, again brought the pressure down still further, but that it recovered slightly at Holloway Bridge before the booster was cut out, and that when it was used to re-start from New Barnet it did not affect the pressure at all. Having reached Hatfield, a station situated on a short stretch of level track, the locomotive started this enormous load by using the booster engine alone. The average speed between King's Cross and Hatfield, 17.6 miles, was 23 miles an hour, including the stops and re-starts, and the booster was used for only 12 minutes during the journey.

Log of experimental test train, 29 July 1924

		Times (pm)	Boiler pressure (lbs per sq in)	
King's Cross	d	12 08	170	
Copenhagen Box	a	12 10	156	
	d	12 14	170	
Caledonian Rd Bridge			142	
Holloway (N London) Br		12 21	145	Booster cut out
New Barnet	a	12 38	160	
	d	12 40	170	
		12 42	—	Booster cut out
Potters Bar	a	12 51	175	
	d	12 52		
½ ml N of Potters Bar		12 53½		Booster cut out
Hatfield	a	1 01		

Four weeks later the engine was tested on a semi-fast train, the 11.30 am from King's Cross to Grantham, with a 12-coach train weighing about 350 tons. There were nine intermediate stops totalling 33 minutes' standing time. In spite of two signal checks before Potters Bar and Hatfield, the train was on time or early at each station, though three of the starts were late. The rapid acceleration due to the use of the booster was very noticeable.

The two test runs suggested that the desired objective of having extra power available when needed had been achieved, but along with further tests they also revealed where improvements were needed. It had at first been intended that the booster was only to be used when the train was starting from rest and that it would be cut out when it was well on the move. In actual operation, however, it was found that when a heavy load was being hauled it was also desirable to re-engage it if a check was experienced while a heavy gradient was being climbed, without the train having to stop first. It was also found that when full power was applied to it there was a tendency to slip. The booster had been designed to be used only in full gear, and this not only made it difficult to bring the gears into mesh while the locomotive was in motion, but also meant that when this did happen the sudden increase of extra tractive force caused slipping. Thirdly, the booster exhaust, as at first designed, tended to choke the main exhaust so that the hot gases from the firebox were not drawn so readily through the boiler tubes and pressure fell too quickly. Fourthly, it was realized that the Westinghouse pump could be discarded and steam used instead to engage the booster gears.

To meet the first problem, the gearing ratio was altered from 2.75:1 to 1.5:1. This, while lessening the booster's tractive force from 8,500 to 4,970 lbs, still left it able to pull sufficiently and removed the tendency to slipping. It also lessened the force of the exhaust so that there was less back-pressure in the smokebox as speed increased. At the same time, the booster's exhaust was rearranged, so that it was no longer directed upwards towards the chimney through an annular outlet around the top of the blast pipe, but mixed first with the exhaust from the engine's main cylinders. The Westinghouse pump had only provided a total of 300 lbs pressure on the plunger which operated the gear engagement system, but when it was removed and steam used instead a much higher force could be exerted, and failure to engage the gears, which had sometimes happened before, was obviated. (Previously the driver had often had to try more than once). When the engine had been remodelled in these ways it was found that the booster could be used at a higher speed without drawing too heavily on the boiler's steam supply, and that it could be cut in at any speed up to 25 miles an hour. Bringing it into action or disengaging it now took much less time — 5 instead of 15 seconds.

Booster-fitted 'Atlantic' No 4419 at the head of the up 'Queen of Scots' Pullman. (NRM)

A test run was made with the locomotive after the modifications had been completed; the section chosen was the main East Coast line between Edinburgh and Berwick-on-Tweed. The train, weighing 350 tons, was stopped on the 1 in 96 gradient of Cockburnspath bank. With the help of the booster it re-started without difficulty, and after a little more than a quarter of a mile had been covered it was possible to notch the main cylinders up to 50 per cent cut-off. The whole bank to Grantshouse station was surmounted satisfactorily. Then the train was taken back again to the foot of the bank it had just climbed, and an attempt was made to start it without the booster. It refused to budge. The booster was then cut in, but disengaged as soon as the train was on the move. Reduction of the cut-of to 50 per cent at the same place as before caused so much deceleration that the booster had to be re-engaged to prevent the train from coming to a stand, and it took three times as long to reach the top of the bank.

The booster having proved itself successful, No 4419 continued for some years to operate express passenger trains. Gresley also built two 2–8–2s with boosters for freight operation, and they too appear to have been successful, coping with 100-wagon trains between Peterborough and London and being able to re-start and accelerate these in difficult places. At 20 miles an hour on an up gradient of 1 in 200 they were able to exert a quarter as much force again as they would have done without boosters.

A few years later, in 1931, Gresley experimentally remodelled two other express engines, 'Z' Class 'Atlantics' of the former North Eastern Railway, Nos 727 and 2171. A fault of No 4419 had been that the cab rode roughly, though an alteration in the method of suspending the booster truck eventually corrected this. However, Gresley wondered whether a quite different arrangement might not secure even better riding, and he came up with the idea of articulating a locomotive to its tender by means of a four-wheel bogie common to both, one of its two axles being booster-driven. He had been able to purchase five booster units at a special price, and fitted three of them to 0–8–4 tank engines of Great Central design to be used in Wath marshalling yard. Of their performance nothing appears to be known, but they seem to have given satisfaction. The remaining two were installed in Nos 727 and 2171. These locomotives were now well advanced in years, having been built in 1911 and 1914 respectively. They were now reconstructed so thoroughly that they no longer resembled the rest of their class. The boilers were new, the firebox was larger, the boiler pressure was increased from 175 to 200 lbs per square inch, and additional superheat was given. As for the booster bogie, it was enormous, with a wheelbase longer than the coupled wheelbase of the locomotive. The booster cylinders were larger than those carried by No 4419 and when in use

Below *Gresley's 2-8-2 freight locomotive No 2393, which was fitted when built with a booster. The steam pipe to the booster engine, less conspicuous than that fitted to 'Atlantic' No 4419, is seen emerging from above the rear coupled wheels. (NRM)*

Bottom *No 2393 at the head of a very heavy freight train near Potters Bar. (LCGB)*

could raise the tractive effort from 22,010 to 27,975 lbs. Each locomotive, tender included, was 9½ tons heavier than before, and the adhesion weight, when the booster was in use, went up to 58.1 tons, part of the weight of the tender being also utilized as well as that of the rear of the locomotive. Tests were carried out with No 727; on level track the heaviest load it could start unaided was just under 500 tons, whereas with booster assistance a load half as heavy again was moved. On a 1 in 70 gradient with a 300-ton train, 18 miles an hour was attained after eight minutes without the booster; when the latter was used 26 miles an hour was reached in less than six minutes.

These engines, also, could therefore be claimed as successes. Nevertheless Gresley never built or remodelled any more 'Atlantics' with boosters; indeed, after a while all three engines had them removed, though to outward appearance they still looked much the same; the long steam pipes which adorned No 4419 and the articulated bogies on Nos 727 and 2171 remained in place. It is not difficult to see why these experiments were not followed up. With unusual and non-standard types, the question of maintenance and repair costs has always to be considered, since these are always higher and have to be set against economies or greater usefulness achievable. In regard to the day-to-day work of these engines, one does not know whether they showed up

The booster mechanism of No 2393 seen after removal of the tender. Note the jointed steam pipe leading to the booster cylinders.
(NRM)

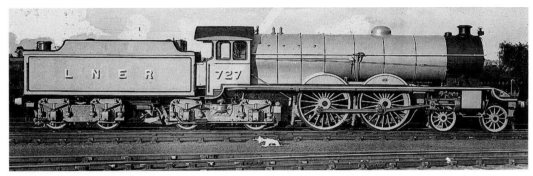

better or worse than their more conventionally constructed fellows. No striking performances by them were ever reported in Cecil J. Allen's articles in *The Railway Magazine*. As booster-assisted engines their lives were short, less than five years. The fact was that on the East Coast main line, sufficient 'Pacifics' had been built to cope with existing express services, even though the latter were being gradually accelerated. Whereas in 1924 Gresley had only 12 4–6–2s of his own design and five of Sir Vincent Raven's, by the beginning of 1938 he had 78, and more were to come. All had adequate adhesion and most were more powerful than the original 12. If there had ever been any question of increasing passenger train loads beyond the 15-coach level, perhaps boosters would have been useful on the 4–6–2s, but train lengths were limited by platform lengths at the main stations, particularly at King's Cross. So the 'Atlantics' were used on lighter trains, such as the 'Queen of Scots' Pullman and the Cambridge Buffet expresses, and on these they still performed magnificently despite their relatively low adhesion, outshining in their old age the achievements of their youth.

Side view of No 727, the North Eastern Railway's 'Z' Class 'Atlantic' rebuilt with an articulated bogie containing a booster element beneath the cab and the front tender. There was not much left of the original 'Z' after the reconstruction. (NRM)

17

Two ultra-high-pressure compound locomotives

The search for greater efficiency through compounding gave rise, as we have seen, to the temperamental three-cylinder engines built by Webb, T.W. Worsdell's two-cylinder locomotives, and the three different four-cylinder tandem compounds constructed by Matthew Holmes and William Dean, and also issued on the Midland Railway in the multiplication of three-cylinder compound 4-4-0s that successfully handled all that line's principal expresses and, later, many of those on the London, Midland & Scottish Railway. Then the practice took an unusual turn in the 'twenties, when two experimental locomotives were built, one on the London & North Eastern Railway, the other on the London, Midland & Scottish Railway. They, too, were compounds, but their boilers, especially that of the second, were subjected to pressures far greater than those of any of the earlier compounds. Planned and constructed from 1924 onwards, they took the rails first at the end of the decade and caused gasps of astonishment among those who saw them. One worked in its original state; the other suffered an unfortunate accident which discouraged its owners from doing more than a little additional testing. Both were later rebuilt on more conventional lines as non-compounds.

*   *   *

The mastermind behind the London & North Eastern experiment was H.N. Gresley, the Chief Mechanical Engineer, whose fitting of boosters to three 'Atlantic' locomotives was described in the previous chapter. By 1924 he had built a fair number of his first batch of 'Pacifics', but they were not doing as well as might have been expected, and the celebrated locomotive exchange with the Great Western the following year, when a 'Pacific'; ran between Paddington and Plymouth and a 'Castle' Class 4-6-0 took its place on the East Coast main line, showed the former up in a poor light and indicated that there was room for improvement both in performance and in fuel consumption. Later modifications were to make the 'Pacifics' the equals of the Great Western engines, but in 1924 this was still in the future, and Gresley's mind turned towards something more radical, the adoption of compounding using very high pressure steam.

That a steam locomotive could be worked more economically with a high-pressure boiler had long been known, and such boilers were already being used in stationary plants and in steamship engine-rooms. A railway engine, however, had to contain everything within the narrow limits of the loading gauge, so considerable difficulties faced any designer who wished to replace the conventional type of steam boiler with a high-pressure water tube boiler of the latest type, small versions of which, as mentioned above in Chapter 12, were already being installed in Sentinel railcars.

Such a boiler did not receive heat in the hitherto customary way in which the hot sides of the firebox at one end and fire tubes taking the hot (but quickly cooling) products of combustion through its middle and lower parts raised the temperature of the water within it to boiling point. Instead, a very large number of tubes branched out from the lower parts of an upper steam drum and connected the latter with water drums below to which the feed water was supplied. The radiant heat from the furnace played directly on these tubes, causing the water within them to boil very rapidly, so that in the upper steam drum steam accumulated at a very high pressure. In fact, the tubes themselves *were* the boiler; the upper drum had no flue-tubes within it and was not at any point in direct contact with the fire. No steam dome was necessary as the top of the drum was well above the level of the boiling water. Fifty years earlier the satisfactory construction of such a boiler would not have been possible, but marine engine firms now had the knowledge and expertise to build one that could safely be used in a steamship — where, however, there were not the restrictions of space which operated on a railway.

In 1924 the Delaware & Hudson Railroad in the United States built a 2-8-0 freight engine using a water tube boiler pessed to 350 lbs per square inch, constructed according to the advice of Yarrow and Company, the well-known marine engineers on Clydeside in Scotland. The steam it generated passed first to a high-pressure cylinder on one side of the locomotive and then to a low-pressure cylinder on the other side. It proved to be successful at the job it was set to do — hauling very heavy freight trains at a low speed — and Gresley, who had been followig its progress, took the hint. The Delaware & Hudson went on to construct three more such engines, two 2-8-0s with boilers pressed to 400 and 500 lbs per square inch respectively, and then built an even larger machine, a 4-8-0, which not only had a water tube boiler pressed to 500 lbs per square inch, but triple expansion cylinders into the bargain. Under test it succeeded in hauling a load of 6,103 tons up a gradient of 1 in 200 at 4½ miles an hour, the dynamometer car showing a drawbar pull of 74,000 lbs. This last development came after Gresley's own high-pressure engine, described below, had been completed; it was the earlier 2-8-0s that had impressed him. These American locomotives without question did what they were asked to do, but they also proved to be very heavy on repairs, so no more were built. They could also not have done what Gresley wished *his* new engine to do — to pull heavy express passenger trains as well as his 'Pacifics', but with a lower consumption of fuel.

To design a water tube boiler that would fit within the British loading gauge took a great deal of contriving, and it was a long while before this aim was achieved. In September 1924 Gresley contacted Mr Harold Yarrow and entered into a three years' partnership with him, which resulted eventually in a patent application being lodged in their joint names covering the boiler itself, along with another covering an arrangement for pre-heating the air supply to the firegrate. Some few months later, Gresley took out in his own name a patent covering the independent operation of the high-pressure and low-pressure cylinder valves.

Principles having been agreed, the next thing was to get the details right. Yarrow and Co undertook to construct the boiler, while Doncaster works provided the specification, and it took over a year before the latter was finally settled, since Gresley made several visits to Glasgow for personal discussions with Yarrow and his staff, and frequently changed his mind between visits. (When the final drawings were presented at Glasgow it was remarked to him that the only unaltered thing in them was the title). As to the rest of the locomotive, that was to be built at Darlington works, and much of the necessary material was ordered in July 1928.

Besides the boiler, other matters had to be determined — in particular the area of the firegrate, the number and sizes of the cylinders, the steam pressure, the actual arrangement of the enormous boiler above the frames and wheels, and the sort of wheeled support the rear of the locomotive was to have. In regard to the firegrate size, Gresley decided it should be the same as in his 'Pacifics', 7 ft by 5½ ft, though Yarrow had suggested it ought to be larger. As to the cylinders, while he had at first determined on three, he finally fixed on four. The inside high-pressure ones were to be quite small, only 12 inches wide, the outside low-pressure ones being 20 inches across; the stroke was to be 26 inches. The steam pressure, at first intended to be 350 lbs per square inch, was increased after some discussion at Glasgow to 450 lbs, with the high pressure ones exhausting into the low-pressure ones at 200 lbs.

How the boiler was to be placed above the frames was a matter needing very careful consideration. It was not just a matter of fitting it beneath the loading gauge. There was also the problem of preventing exhaust steam from obscuring the driver's vision when the locomotive was travelling at speed on a low cut-off. Gresley took counsel with Professor W.E. Dalby, of the London City and Guilds Engineering College, about this, as also about the proportions between the high-pressure and low-pressure cylinder capacities. Dalby had a wooden model of the engine made, which was placed in a 50 miles-an-hour air stream while powdered chalk was blown upwards through the chimney; the course of the chalk particles was observed and adjustments were made to the shape of the front until the chalk was seen to clear the cab windows. In effect, therefore, the front end of the engine was designed as a smoke-deflector, and this gave it the appearance of having been deliberately streamlined, which it was not. The final arrangement removed the chimney from sight altogether; it nestled down at the far end of a V-shaped scoop and could not be seen except from the front — a peculiarity which caused much comment.

To support the rear of the engine Gresley had originally intended to fix a two-wheel truck similar to that used on his 'Pacifics'. However, the length of the boiler eventually made it necessary for four wheels to be employed. Accordingly *two* trailing trucks were used, rather than a four-wheel bogie, the front one having less side play than the rear one. This was to spark off quite a lot of pointless controversy about whether the locomotive was a 4-6-4 or a 4-6-2-2.

Once the frames, motion, cylinders, etc had been completed, they were sent to Glasgow for the boiler to be fixed in position above them (though the two middle driving wheels were kept back at Darlington so that there would be no difficulty in negotiating low-radius curves on Yarrow's premises). Boiler and cylinders had already been tested at double the working pressure of 450 lbs and found satisfactory. Once the completely assembled engine was back at Darlington, a new tender of the 'corridor' type was attached to it — an indication that it was to be employed hauling the non-stop 'Flying Scotsman', along with 'Pacifics' similarly so fitted. It was then painted, not in LNER green but in lined-out battleship grey, and given no name, but numbered 10000. It then left the works to undergo testing before being allowed to haul any scheduled express passenger trains, and not until the spring of 1930 was it seen in action on any regular services.

The photographs overleaf show the appearance of the water tube boiler before it was installed on the engine. Cecil J. Allen, who included

No 10000, Gresley's high-pressure water tube boiler 4-6-4 as completed in its original form, with corridor tender. (NRM)

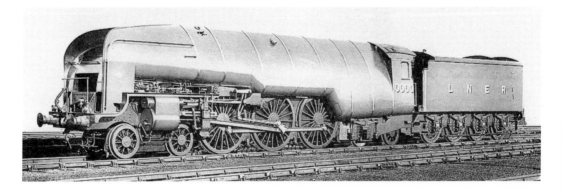

a description of the locomotive in his regular 'British Locomotive Practice and Performance' article in *The Railway Magazine* for June 1930, gave a clear account of it, and of how it raised steam, which is worth quoting in full:

'The water tube boiler consists, first of all, of two water drums on either side of the firebox, each 11 ft long and 18 in diameter, inclined upwards, with a steam drum 3 ft diameter by 28 ft long, which is located along the centre line of the engine at the highest point permitted by the loading gauge. Ahead of the firebox are two other water drums at a higher level, 13 ft 6 in long by 1 ft 7 in, which are connected by 444 2 in and 74 2½ in tubes with the forward end of the steam drum. Suitable casing carries the products of combustion through these nests of water tubes — the ordinary process of steam raising in a locomotive boiler being exactly reversed, in that heat is applied from outside to the water within the tubes instead of from the inside of the boiler tubes to the water surrounding them — to the smokebox. Air for combustion enters by three rectangular openings in the smokebox front and is thus passed along the boiler from front to back, becoming heated in its passage well above the atmospheric temperature — a feature making for economy — and serving on the other hand to protect the boiler lagging from excessive heat.'

A number of other unusual features in this locomotive call for mention. Firstly, the Walschaerts' valve gears for the high-pressure and low-pressure cylinders could be operated independently of one another. In the cab there were two different controls, both steam-operated. The *reversing* determined in what direction the locomotive was to travel and also the cut-off in the low-pressure cylinders. The *expansion* gear altered the cut-off in the high-pressure cylinders with respect to the low-pressure cut-off. So a variety of cut-off positions, different for each pair of cylinders, could be employed. Both reversing gear and expansion gear handles were placed side by side in a quadrant plate in the cab.

Secondly, the smokebox was much larger than usual — 16 feet in length — and the front end of the steam drum extended forwards into

Rear right-hand aspect of No 10000's water tube boiler at Yarrow's factory in Glasgow before installation in the locomotive. (Mitchell, Library, Glasgow)

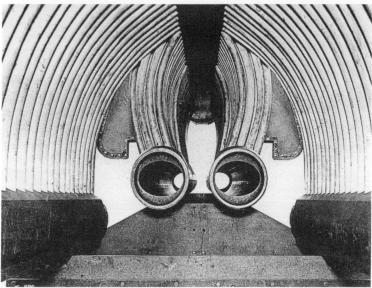

Another view of No 10000's water tube boiler, taken from approximately the position of the fire door (Mitchell Library, Glasgow)

Right *The cab of No 10000, showing the rear end of the upper steam drum and the triple set of levers in quadrants for operating the valve gearing.* (Mitchell Library, Glasgow)

Below *The outer cladding partly in position over the water tube boiler after it had been fixed to the engine framing. The central driving wheels are missing so that the engine could negotiate sharp curves in the factory precincts.* (Mitchell Library, Glasgow)

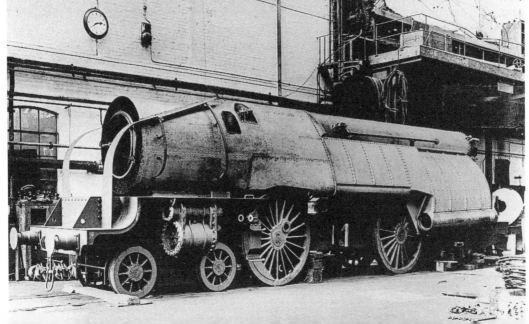

its interior; however, this projecting part contained not steam but a reservoir of feed water which was here pre-heated before it passsed to the four water drums. At either side on the back of the smokebox were two regulator valves; the left-hand one, 3 inches in diameter, passed steam to the high-pressure cylinders, while that on the right, only 1 inch in diameter, fed the low-pressure cylinders by way of the intermediate receiver when the engine was starting; once it had been closed, full compounding began.

Thirdly, there was the special system for pre-heating the air supply to the firebox grate, mentioned above by Mr Allen. This air intake, cold when it entered, was then guided along a space between the inner boiler casing and the outer casing until it was redirected downwards at the rear to enter the ashpan, being by now almost as hot as boiling water. A peculiarity of this device was that when the engine was going forwards at speed, the outer boiler casing could be observed slightly to expand and contract rhythmically in a wave passing backwards towards the cab, with a movement like the peristaltic action of the human intestine as it forces its contents along — if so ignoble a simile may be permitted!

Once it had been put on the road for testing, it was to be expected that a locomotive with so many unusual features would suffer teething troubles. Quite a number *were* experienced, large and small, and to enumerate them all would be tedious. Runs on test tains between December 1929 and January 1930 seem to have passed without incident, but on 23 February, when a test load of 406 tons was worked from Edinburgh to Perth and back by way of Dunfermline, No 10000 did not show up at all well. It slipped badly when starting from Edinburgh Waverley, on an admittedly greasy rail, and managed to attain no higher speed than 58 miles an hour at the bottom of the Turnhouse dip. A slight signal delay at Dalmeny, and a stop on the Forth Bridge for photographs to be taken, put the train a quarter of an hour behind time at Dunfermline. It then proceeded to lose another 6½ minutes to Perth, largely because of over-caution on the part of the driver, T. Blades, who did not know the road. The return journey was even more of an anti-climax; again the engine slipped badly on starting and went on to lose 17 minutes before Waverley was reached. However over-cautious the driver may have been, it cannot have helped him to have had as many as 17 people on his footplate — including Gresley and his two daughters — while climbing the 1 in 75 bank from Bridge of Earn to Glenfarg. This unremarkable out-and-home performance required the expenditure of as much as 64.2 lbs of coal per engine mile, which boded ill for a locomotive whose peculiar features were intended to promote economical working.

During the next five years or so, No 10000 spent something like five-eighths of its time in Darlington works, returning between many spells of workshop attention to run on service trains. Among the alterations made on these occasions were the reduction of superheater surface area (it had been found that it regularly over-heated the steam), the fitting of more efficient water injectors and the lining up of the high-pressure cylinders from 12 to 10 inches in diameter (as it had been found they were doing more than their fair share of work). The engine's performance between its spells of major and minor surgery was never very distinguished, either on test or with regular passenger trains. Quite early in its career, probably in the spring of 1930, Cecil J. Allen timed a run behind it between Darlington and York, with a 440-ton load on a 43-minute schedule for the 44.1 miles. It took just over 44 minutes after a slight signal check on the approach to York. Allen was impressed that with a load so much greater than was customary with this train it had come so near to keeping time. 'Barely a single minute had to go against the engine .... a most successful début'. To the present writer, who in his train-timing days more than once bettered 44 minutes with an equal load behind one of the 'Pacifics' in its original state, No 10000's performance on this occasion does not seem much to crow about.

From August 1932 onwards, the engine's performances improved and became more predictable. A series of test runs showed it could now haul trains of 350 tons or thereabouts with a coal consumption of about 44 lbs a mile — a great reduction on the figures of two and a half years earlier. Gresley, still hopeful that his grey elephant might yet turn out to be a racehorse after all, continued to order one modification after another, including the fitting of a double chimney. But he had now designed and built his masterpiece, the streamlined 'A4', which was making locomotive history by its running with the 'Silver Jubilee' between London and Newcastle in four hours. So in August 1935 he decided to rebuild No 10000 as a streamliner. It entered Darlington works for the last time, remained there for some months, was then transferred to Doncaster and was there rebuilt as a three-cylinder non-compound locomotive with a conventional boiler. As reconstructed it resembled the streamlined 'A4' 'Pacifics' except in retaining its four trailing wheels beneath the firebox and cab. It looked like a racehorse at last. However, it does not seem to have made any record runs, though on one occasion it proved its capacity for speed by working the up 'Silver Jubilee' and arriving at King's Cross on time. It appears to have been popular with drivers because it ran smoothly, but less so with firemen because of the extra distance, as compared with other 'Pacifics', between the shovelling plate and the firebox door. Its trailing carrying wheels also had an unfortunate propensity towards running hot. However, it lasted until 1959.

So ended Gresley's boldest experiment. If it could have proved itself capable of doing what it had been designed to do — burning significantly less coal for the same amount of work in comparison with the 'Pacific' types, perhaps more might have been built. As it was, faults were always being corrected, and meanwhile the engines it had been designed to improve upon were themselves vastly impoved. So in the

After its final rebuilding as a 4-6-4 streamliner generally similar to the 'A4 Pacifics', No 10000 is turned outside King's Cross. (LCGB)

end it turned out not be a pointer to the future, but a blank wall at the end of a blind alley .

*   *   *

While No 10000 was undergoing its double gestation at Darlington and Glasgow, another monster was coming to birth at the latter place, in the works of the North British Locomotive Company, where it was being produced for the London, Midland & Scottish Railway. It was to have a less fortunate career than its LNER fellow, and was never used to haul fare-paying passengers. It was a variant of the 'Royal Scot' type of 4–6–0, built by the same firm which constructed the other 'Royal Scots', and the inspiration for its special features came not from America but Germany. Prophetically looking forward to a certain disastrous day in February 1930, it was named *Fury* when completed, after a former 2–2–0 on the Liverpool & Manchester Railway which had been built 99 years earlier; brass medallion (see the adjacent photograph) under the nameplate explained the association and showed a diagram of the former engine.

Dr Wilhelm Schmidt, the inventor in Germany of the fire tube superheater for steam locomotives, had further pursued his researches and devised a new type of steam-raising equipment in which steam at a very high pressure was produced, not through the boiler being in direct contact with the heat of the firebox or of fire tubes leading from it, but by means of a closed circuit of distilled water which was vaporized in a system of tubing and drums. The tubing, receiving radiant heat directly from the burning fuel in the firebox, boiled its contents to a pressure of between 1,400 and 1,800 lbs per square inch; this ultra-high-pressure steam then circulated within a high-pressure boiler drum, vaporizing the water within it and itself condensing to run back again as water to the lower part of its own circuit, when it was re-used. Thus there were in effect two water boilers, one heated by the firebox which passed on steam to heat the other.

Schmidt believed that the usual methods of boiler construction could not safely be used once a pressure of 570 lbs per square inch had been exceeded. Not only would special steels need to be used, but there ought to be no direct heating of the boiler's sensitive parts through immediate contact with the fire or with hot gases proceeding from it. So heating should be indirect, in the manner indicated above. He envisaged a locomotive with two boilers, one of the usual kind with fire tubes, which produced low-pressure steam, and the other of the kind he had invented which produced steam at a much higher pressure. The engine would of course be a compound — or perhaps would be more properly styled a 'semi-compound' in which the high-pressure steam, having operated the high-pressure cylinder or cylinders, then went on to mix with the low-pressure steam, imparting some of its heat to it before the low-pressure cylinders were reached.

The low-pressure boiler, besides producing low-pressure steam, would also act as a water purifier for the high-pressure steam drum, since the latter would receive its water from the former. Any scale or deposit from the water would remain within the low-pressure boiler, which would of course be cleaned out at intervals in the usual way. Water so injected into the high-pressure drum, therefore, would be almost completely pure. As for the water in the ultra-high-pressure closed circuit, no question of deposit would arise since it would be pure distilled water.

A locomotive on Schmidt's principles was built in Germany and exhibited at the Munich Railway Exhibition in 1925, where it attracted the attention of the Superheater Company of Great Britain. This firm secured a licence from the Schmidt'sche Heissdampft Gesellschaft to build a prototype locomotive of the same sort in Great Britain. A little later the French State Railways, SNCF, obtained a similar permission and eventually produced a 4-8-2 prototype. Both the German and French engines were rebuilds, but in Great Britain it was decided to construct a new engine, and a three-cornered agreement was made, which was expressed in the North British Locomotive Company's order book was follows:

No 6399's nameplate, showing the engraving of the first Fury, a 2-2-0 built for the Liverpool & Manchester Railway in 1831. (Mitchell Library, Glasgow)

> '*L.858*: — Date ordered, Dec. 15, 1928: London Midland and Scottish Railway: One 4-6-0 Passenger Engine (No Tender) Royal Scot class: Fitted with High Pressure Boiler in accordance with Superheater Company's design, now on order under D 3745. General Conditions of L.M. & Scottish specification to offer. As per Offer of 26th. ult. & 11th. inst.'

The design of the boiler was the work of the Superheater Company, closely advised by the German firm of Henschel of Kassel, which had built the locomotive exhibited at Munich. The rest of the engine was, as one might say, 'Royal Scot minus boiler', and the North British

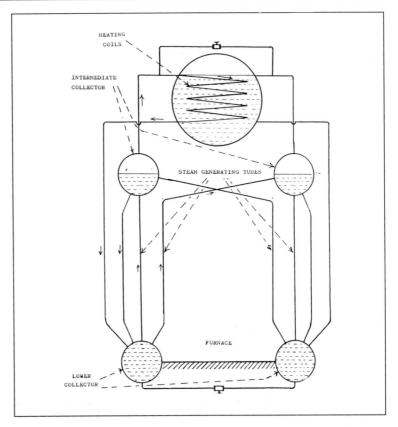

Locomotive Company assembled the whole machine in their Glasgow works for use on the London, Midland & Scottish Railway, on whose metals the testing eventually took place. The actual date of delivery to the LMS was 30 January 1930. This was quick work, but the North British Locomotive Company could move fast when required, as had been shown by the rapid way in which they had built the original 'Royal Scots'.

The accompanying line drawing shows how the water and steam circulated in the ultra-high-pressure closed circuit. Steam from water which had boiled in the tubes at the sides, back and top of the firebox rose first into the equalizing inter-drums and went on from there into the main steam drum, where it gave up most of its heat to the water in that drum, causing it to boil, by passing through an evaporative element, 12 tubes arranged in zigzag bends. It condensed at the bottom of the element and then descended to the foundation ring. (The word 'ring' is something of a misnomer; it was a hollow rectangular tube of square section which surrounded the grate area, into which all the pipes were let). From the ring it was again pushed upwards by the later increments of condensed water, rose up into the tubes beside and above

the fire, and so repeated the circuit. The line drawing is purely diagrammatic in order to explain the circulation; what the system in fact looked like can be seen in the adjacent photograph, which also shows the space between the tubes at the back, left for the fire door.

The main steam drum, which produced steam at 950 lbs per square inch, was placed as high as the loading gauge permitted. It was built of nickel steel and was 15 ft 2½ in long, the rearward end, which had a manhole for inspection purposes, projecting slightly back into the cab. For most of its length its diameter was 3 ft 2 in, but the front end was only half that width; in appearance it resembled the familiar Thermos vacuum flask, greatly enlarged. The low-pressure boiler, ahead of it, was also made of nickel steel, with mild steel front and back plates, and was heated entirely by means of fire tubes which led from a combustion chamber at the front end of the furnace. It was a domed drum 5 ft 7½ in in diameter and 8 ft 8 in long, with a 3 ft 3 in backward extension from its lower part, at the end of which was the back tube-plate. Steam from the dome met exhaust steam from the high-pressure cylinder in a mixing chamber and then passed to the outside low-pressure cylinders. Steam from both boilers was superheated in the usual manner within

No 6399's high-pressure water tube boiler under construction at the North British Locomotive Company's works, showing clearly the upper steam drum, the intermediate drums, the water tubes and the foundation ring beneath them. (Mitchell Library, Glasgow)

No 6399's forward low-pressure boiler after being fitted to the frames at the NBL works. Its lower backward extension can be clearly seen. (NRM)

fire tubes. The low-pressure boiler also fed water at high temperature into the steam drum, pumped in by a pump on one side of the smokebox. It received its own feed water from the tender supply by means of a similar pump on the other side of the smokebox. Practically all the impurities in the feed water were deposited on the interior surfaces of the low-pressure boiler, so that very little, it was hoped, would need to be removed from the inside of the high-pressure drum. Admission of steam to all three cylinders was through two regulators, from drum and boiler respectively, through a high-pressure and a low-pressure valve, both being operated with the same regulator handle in the cab.

The whole arrangement was even more complicated than that of Gresley's No 10000, but it was confidently expected that economies would be experienced, both in fuel consumption and in time spent in maintenance and repair, and that the shorter time spent on the latter would mean an improved utilization of the locomotive. As already mentioned, the actual construction went ahead very rapidly, and there was much interest and enthusiasm shown on the part of all three companies involved, who were jointly promoting the venture — the railway company, the builders and the Superheater Company. Slightly less than a year after the original order was placed, the engine was completed, despite many incidental problems that had arisen during its building, and it was ready for testing.

On 6 December 1929, the first official tests were carried out, steam being raised for the first time, and various important persons from all three interested companies were there to observe. However, the event was an anti-climax; the high-pressure regulator began to leak at 500 lbs pressure and modifications had to be carried out. The following day steam was again raised, and when it had reached its maximum in the high-pressure drum the safety valves opened with a noise like a bomb exploding. Everyone present ran for cover, while the valves continued blowing off until the pressure had fallen to 600 lbs. Over the following eight weeks, one small fault after another was corrected and the two regulators at last consented to behave properly. The engine was then moved from the works, first to Polmadie shed and then, on 10 February 1930, on to the main line for a trial run as far as Carstairs. For the engine itself, now named and numbered 6399, and for the footplate crew, it was an appointment with destiny.

What happened that day may be described in the bald factual account given at a later Enquiry by one of the four men who were on the footplate, F.J. Pepper, the LMS Company's representative. Also with him were Driver Hall, Fireman Blair, and the Superheater Company's representative, Mr Louis Schofield.

'The engine left the shed at about 10.30 am, reaching the main line about 10.40 am. Driver Donald Hall was in charge. About ten minutes before the accident occurred both Mr Schofield and I had occasion to examine the gauge glass of the water in the closed circuit. The pressure then showed about 950 lbs, which is well below the maximum of which this circuit is capable. The pressures in the various boilers were quite consistent with each other throughout the journey. Everything appeared to be going well ... Before reaching Carstairs the pressure in the closed circuit had risen to 1,000 lbs.

'The accident occurred when the engine was passing the end of the up platform at Carstairs. There was a great rush of steam from the firebox. The fire was blown out on to the footplate with great force. The engine was then running at about 6 or 8 mph.

'Immediately the rush of steam occurred I tried to get off the footplate, but my leg jammed in the doorway. I caught hold of the roof of the cab and pulled myself clear of the footplate until the engine came to a stand. It did this about half-way through the station. I heard the brake being applied. I had great difficulty in getting Mr Schofield off the footplate. He was immediately attended to by the station staff ... I heard afterwards that Mr Schofield had died of his injuries on the following day.

'I am satisfied that the running and working of the engine were quite in order.'

No 6399 Fury ready for steaming at the North British Locomotive Company's works in Glasgow in early in 1930.
(Mitchell Library, Glasgow)

A later note added:

'Fireman dived from engine head first & stunned & slightly hurt. Driver escaped force of blast from firebox, raised himself clear of footplate by holding cab roof & then reached & applied brake handle.'

Accounts of this event have differed and I have chosen to take the one given by Mr Pepper at the Enquiry. He himself was scalded, but not apparently severely, as he was able to extricate Mr Schofield from the footplate. The driver suffered slight injuries, while the fireman suffered some broken bones. The unfortunate Mr Schofield was literally in the line of fire when one of the tubes at the top of the firebox suddenly burst (see the adjacent illustration) and blew steam at about 1,000 lbs per square inch pressure down on to the fire, forcing much of it out through the open fire door. He was rushed to Edinburgh by an engine hauling a single van, but nothing could be done for him and he died the following day. At the Public Enquiry held at Lanark on 21 March, the jury returned a verdict of 'Accidental Death' and the widow later received compensation in an out-of-court settlement.

It was never definitely established what caused the tube to burst. However, a similar accident, though fortunately without tragic consequence, occurred to the French 4-8-2 which, as mentioned above, had also been reconstructed on the Schmidt system, while it was

hauling a train between Laroche and Dijon. Subsequent microscopic examination of the metal of the high-pressure tubes showed that in places exposed to the fire a coarsening of the microstructure had developed. Something like that may have happened in the closed circuit of *Fury*.

The damaged tube was replaced and the engine was towed to Derby

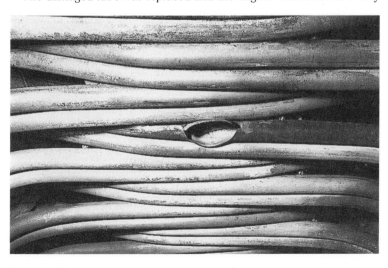

Above *A magnificent view, taken with a full-plate camera, of the LMS experimental high pressure compound express locomotive* Fury, *built in 1929 and seen here in the yard outside the works of the North British Locomotive Company, Glasgow, immediately after construction. The man and woman on the footplate are probably Sir Henry Fowler, Chief Mechanical Engineer on the LMS at the time, and Lady Fowler (see Chapter 17).* (Mitchell Library, Glasgow)

Left *Photograph of the interior of No 6399's firebox taken after the Carstairs accident, showing where the blow-out occurred.* (Mitchell Library, Glasgow)

works. It has frequently been stated that it never again ran under its own steam, but at least seven trial runs are now known to have been made with a dynamometer car attached behind the engine, and there may have been more. On each of these occasions something went wrong, though never catastrophically so. The first test was in July 1932, the last in March 1934. A representative of the Superheater Company was on the footplate on each occasion, and no doubt kept his fingers crossed. The precaution had been taken of arranging that the firebox should close automatically after each firing. The upshot was that a report was made that 'the engine could in no way be modifed, and was definitely unfit for ordinary service'. So it was sent back to Derby for the last time, and when it next appeared it was as a rebuild. The Schmidt steam-raising system had been discarded and a taper boiler had been fitted; it was now a three-cylinder simple engine, the very successful prototype of the rebuilt 'Royal Scots' which followed it. Like No 10000, a large part of it had lived to run again.

No further ultra-high-pressure locomotives were built on any British railway. The Schmidt system did not live up to its promise. The first locomotive built in Germany on this pattern, while never experiencing any disastrous accident, never produced the expected savings in coal consumption. So there was no incentive to continue with experimentation.

18

Stanier's 'Turbomotive'

Examples have already been given of how technological advances in stationary steam plants and marine engines provoked attempts to apply them to railway locomotives in regard to compounding and the use of water tube boilers. A third possibility was to apply the turbine principle, in which steam is introduced not into a relatively slow-moving reciprocating system of cylinders, pistons, connecting rods and cranks, but instead directed against the vanes of a number of wheels in succession which in consequence move very fast indeed. Such an arrangement allowed the steam to expend practically all its force pressing against one vane after another, and resulted in a completely even torque being given to the turning axle instead of the continually varying one inevitable with a reciprocating engine, so that the vibration caused by the former vanishes completely, along with the exhaust beat. The Royal Navy went over to turbine propulsion in its large capital vessels several years before the start of the First World War, as did other navies also, including Germany's. In consequence their decks made much steadier gun-platforms, and it became possible to train the huge guns to fire accurately at targets as much as ten miles away — as happened at the Battle of Jutland in 1916.

There could be no doubt that if turbines could be applied to steam locomotion there would be a number of advantages, but, as with the provision of water tube boilers, difficulties arose due to the necessity to keep everything within the limitations of the loading gauge. Only one 'turbomotive' was ever built in Great Britain under a railway company's auspices, and it proved much more successful in operation than most of the other experiments so far described. Had it not been for the outbreak of the Second World War, which came when various modifications had been made to obviate the original difficulties, others might have been built to match the prototype.

There had been turbine-driven experiments before, though these did not originate within railway workshops but were organized and financed by private persons, and so fall outside the remit of this book. All were 'turbo-electric' locomotives, the turbines generating electricity which in turn drove electric motors, in much the same way as a diesel-electric locomotive functions. Their developers borrowed a railway, so to speak, to try them out on. The first, the Reid-Ramsey locomotive built by the North British Locomotive Company in 1910, was tried out on the North Eastern Railway, but was not considered successful and was set aside; parts of it were later used in the Reid-MacLeod turbine condensing locomotive built in 1924. Two other locomotives similar in principle were also tried out, in 1923 and 1926, on the London, Midland & Scottish Railway. These all flowered briefly and then disappeared. One difficulty had been the fact that, like turbine-driven stationary and steamship installations, they condensed their steam for re-use and this made them longer and heavier than was convenient.

In 1932, however, a Swedish railway constructed a locomotive with a turbine drive which dispensed with a condenser altogether. It was an unconventionally constructed machine in which the actual turbine mechanism was placed in front of the smokebox. This resulted in the locomotive itself being that much longer than otherwise, but because the water consumption was only moderate, a tender could be attached which was that amount shorter than usual, so the whole machine was not too large to go on a turntable. W.A. Stanier, the Chief Mechanical Engineer of the LMS, heard about it and paid a visit to Sweden with his Chief Draughtsman in the autumn of 1932 together with two friends who were engineers in Metropolitan-Vickers. All were very favourably impressed by its performance and thought a similar experiment should be tried in Great Britain. Financially the times were difficult, but the LMS Board nevertheless gave consent, despite economy being the order of the day, for a prototype turbine-driven locomotive to be constructed. Stanier had already begun the construction of his first two 'Princess' 'Pacifics', and he set his design team to work to build the third as a turbine engine.

Stanier's 'Turbomotive' as first built. The long casing above the left-hand driving wheels housed the controls for the forward-driven turbine. (NRM)

Certain advantages were expected from such a locomotive. Compared with one having reciprocating motion, it should be possible for it to exert a higher tractive effort without the adhesion weight needing to be

greater, since with the more even torque the tendency to slipping would be much less. The pull on the drawbar, too, would be more even. There would be no 'hammer-blow' on the rails since there would be no reciprocating parts. Steam could exhaust at something much nearer to atmospheric pressure. With no need for as many large moving parts as a reciprocating system, there should be less wear and tear, so that time spent in the repair shops would be reduced and less lubrication would be necessary (although on that score a turbine moving at a very high speed needed very thorough lubrication, in a very different manner from the oiling required by the sliding surfaces of a conventionally driven locomotive, and it will be seen below how this problem was met).

However, against these 'pros' a 'con' had to be set. A turbine engine was not suitable for a service in which the demands for power were continually varying. For services with many stops, or for shunting duties, its built-in sophistications were irrelevant. It was useful when a long-continued and even expenditure of force was required, as with a ship at sea. In a locomotive it could only be used with advantage on a long-distance haul with few stops. However, the LMS had many of them on its passenger services linking London with Manchester, Liverpool and Glasgow.

When No 6202 finally emerged from Derby works it did not look all that much different from No 6200 *The Princess Royal*. Apart from the lack of a nameplate (it never carried one during its service as a 'turbomotive') one would have noticed the absence of outside cylinders, connecting rods and valve gear. The wheels were coupled as with an inside-cylinder engine. Circumnavigating it from the left-hand side, one would observe a long box-like housing extending from the smokebox to the front of the cab and covering the tops of the wheels where wheel

Front right-hand view of No 6202 showing the casing over the reverse drive turbine. (NRM)

splashers would normally have been. In the usual place for a left-hand outside cylinder there was a large bulbous covering extending downwards between the wheels of the front bogie. A double, not a single, chimney surmounted the smokebox. Proceeding round the engine, on the other side one saw a similar bulbous casing above and between the bogie wheels, but the box-like housing above it was only a few feet long, so on this side the expected wheel-splashers appeared. Apart from these differences the locomotive resembled its fellow 'Princesses' — unless one chanced to observe it hauling a train at speed. Then one would notice that a kind of hinged lid, resembling that over the keys of a piano, was opened upwards through 45 degrees in order to catch air, which was then passed through a radiator which cooled the oil lubricating the turbine.

The propulsive elements of the locomotive, the turbines themselves, were out of sight. There were two of them, a large one for forward movement and a small one for reversing. The former was within the before-mentioned bulbous covering on the left-hand side, and consisted of an axle holding 16 vane-wheels of increasing diameters from one end to the other. Steam entered at the end where the smallest wheel was and passed through the whole system, playing upon the vanes and forcing them to rotate before finally escaping beyond the largest sixteenth wheel and passing to the blast pipes. An outlet about a quarter of a way along allowed steam to 'bleed' out in sufficient quantity to heat the feed water for the boiler. The steam which went the whole way gave up so much of its force that when it emerged from the turbine its pressure was only a couple of pounds per square inch above that of the atmosphere, but this was enough, escaping towards the double chimney through twin blastpipes, to effect the necessary vacuum in the smokebox.

The reverse turbine resembled the forward one in pattern and was mounted in the same position on the opposite side of the locomotive. It was not intended to be used for haulage but only when running light or during station movements.

Both turbines ran at high speed, so their turning movement was transmitted to the front coupled axle first through a gear box and then through a shaft running along the centre line of the locomotive. The gearing of the forward turbine allowed the engine to proceed at 90 miles an hour when the former was rotating at top speed, at over 200 revolutions a second. A clutch was installed in the drive from the reverse turbine so that the latter during forward movement was prevented from revolving; in rearward movement, however, the forward turbine was not cut out but simply went round backwards.

No 6202 required a completely different method of driving from that used in more conventional machines. The usual type of reverser and cut-off controller was missing, for there was no cut-off to modify, and for reversing one simply shut off one turbine and applied steam to the other. The sort of fine tuning possible with a cylinder-driven locomotive could not be achieved. The regulator had either to be off or on — in the latter case with one, two or three admission valves open. Steam from the boiler passed through the regulator opening, the superheater and the admission valves, did its work on the vanes of the turbine and then exhausted. There was no question of ensuring that its expansive force was properly utilized; that happened in any case. The locomotive naturally 'felt' different in handling; the exhaust was continuous, not intermittent, there were no 'puffs' from the chimney and the footplate was almost as steady as the interior of a coach. The incidental noises which told the driver of any other locomotive how fast he was going were absent. Another problem was that the very light exhaust tended to hang around the boiler top and obscure forward visibility.

Because of their enormous rate of revolution when the locomotive was travelling fast, the revolving surfaces of the turbines and their gears needed to be very well oiled. They were totally enclosed and lubricated under pressure, oil being forced in through pumps. This, continually circulating, became hot and had to be continually cooled by passing through a radiator that itself was cooled by air caught through the already-mentioned 'piano-front' opening below the smokebox. In practice it was found that a very little steam became mixed with the oil; something like a gallon of water had to be drained from the sump at the end of each day. Every 6,000 miles the oil was changed completely. Other parts of the engine were of course oiled in the ordinary way.

Once the locomotive had been completed there was, rather surprisingly, no extended period of initial testing. It was put on the road in June 1935 and set to do the double journey daily between London and Liverpool. It covered over 6,000 miles on this service when a leakage of oil from the turbine units occasioned its removal for repairs, and it spent four weeks away from its duties. This was the first of a long series of absences, of which more is said below; while in operation it had proved satisfactory enough. In May, and later in October, 1936 it was officially tested out against its fellow 'Pacifics' Nos 6210 and 6212 on through journeys from Euston to Glasgow with heavy trains, and the following June it was again similarly tested, though this time on its own. The results were somewhat inconclusive. It appeared to be much the same as the others in regard to haulage capacity and economy of working; the former appeared to be somewhat higher than that of the other two 'Pacifics', but the coal and water consumptions were about the same — between 40 and 50 lbs of the former and 36 to 39 gallons of the latter per mile, with loads varying between 470 and 560 tons. Purely on the basis of these tests, obviously no case could be made for any multiplication of the type; the expected economies were not being seen. The engine could indeed pull harder but it was not cheaper to run.

It also had to spend a great deal of time being repaired; over its whole career as a turbine-driven engine, 14 years in all, it was out of use for more than five. In almost every case it was the turbine transmission that was at fault, either the motors themselves (more often the reverse one), the oiling system or the gearing and shafting. During periods of service in between these 16 occasions of different duration it performed well enough and was liked by those who drove and fired it, though they were not happy with the way that drifting exhaust obscured the view ahead and also penetrated the cab to make it somewhat dirtier than those of other 'Pacifics'. It was better at climbing gradients than the other 4-6-2s. During its visits to the repair shops some alterations were made to meet the complaints of the footplate staff; deflector plates were added to lift the exhaust clear of the cab, and a speedometer was fitted.

Few records of its day-to-day performance exist, and so far as one knows it broke no records. At the beginning of the Second World War it was withdrawn from service, since the works personnel, involved with necessary war work, could not spare the time to give it the specialist repairs it needed. However, it was put back into traffic in July 1941, when every engine that could move at all was pressed into service in the national interest. On one occasion after its return to service Cecil J. Allen enjoyed an unexpected run behind it at the head of an enormous wartime train between Crewe and Watford, as related in his book *British Pacific Locomotives*:

'My liveliest recollection of the "Turbo" is that of travelling up one evening from Crewe, during the late war, with a railway chief engineer who later became a member of the Railway Executive; we had spent the day at a Midland steelworks, and it had been one of most uncomfortably high wind, which by now was beginning to blow itself out. From Crewe we were to take the combined Liverpool and Manchester "diner", an exceedingly heavy train, and my heart sank when I saw No 6202 rolling up the platform at the head of the Liverpool portion. "I'm afraid we're going to lose time", I remarked to my companion, thereby presenting him with a joke against myself which he used for a long time afterwards.

For actually No 6202 proceeded to gain 11½ minutes from Crewe to Watford, and that despite two signal checks and a train made up to 17 vehicles, of 560 tons tare and fully 610 tons gross weight! True, the 168-min wartime schedule then in force for the 140.55 miles was easy enough, but we cut it to 156 min 29 sec, or 153 min net, ran 96 miles of the journey at an average of just over 60 mph, and all without exceeding 66 mph at any point. A particularly good effort was to cover the 15.0 miles from Bletchley up to Tring at an average of 56.8 mph.'

The general picture one gets of No 6202 during 1935-1939 is that of a locomotive fully the equal of its 'Princess' partners in haulage power and economy of working, but which needed much longer periods off duty for repairs, which took it out of service for an undue time, and which were of a very specialized nature. A vicious circle in fact existed. Had it been possible to keep spare parts in sufficient quantity, repairs

could have been carried out in far less time. Had there been a dozen or so 'turbomotives' in existence, no doubt spare turbines could have been stocked, and when one went wrong a replacement could have been fitted in a few days. As things were, with only a prototype to be considered, it took far longer to put matters right. Replacing damaged turbines, in particular, meant reference to the makers Metro-Vickers for advice and help, and the special manufacture of this part or that. This is the trouble with any prototype, as long as it remains a single example of its kind, however successful it may be in traffic. When it goes wrong it cannot be quickly repaired, so it actually pays to use a less efficient engine which can be put back into service more quickly.

Quite possibly more 'turbomotives' might have been built, enough to make it worth while keeping a stock of expensive spare parts, if it had

Top *A later view of the 'Turbomotive' after it had been fitted with a domed boiler and a larger superheater in 1936.* (NRM)

Above *No 6202, now fitted with smoke deflectors, leaving Euston at the head of the 8.30 am express to Liverpool in May 1947.* (LCGB)

not been for the outbreak of the Second World War, which caused the postponement of everything that was not directly related to the requirements of the war. The 'turbomotive' had had only four years in which to prove itself. However, one has also to remember the tendency of the human mind to reject the unfamiliar. The fact was that the conventional type of steam locomotive had been in existence and had developed for so long, and was in general so reliable and versatile, that it had acquired, as it were, an enormous momentum, and anything better than a reciprocating engine with cylinders and cranks had to be so remarkably better that its impact on contemporary engineers could jolt them out of their presuppositions. O.V.S. Bulleid was later to find, when he tried in a desperate race against time to design the engine of the future (as related below in Chapter 20), that brilliant ideas were not enough. You cannot stop a juggernaut so easily. When, after the formation of British Railways, the building of a new standard range of locomotives was contemplated, no one thought in terms of a radical departure from existing practice. 'It's the old-time religion and it's good enough for me!' was the prevailing attitude. No tampering with received doctrine: just modify the established practice a little.

No 6202 lingered on into the post-war years and was duly nationalized. During November 1949 it suffered a final mishap when its turbine failed once more while working the 8.30 am from Euston to Liverpool, and it was sent for repair. This time a much more drastic surgery was performed; it was reconstructed as a reciprocating engine and when completed was something of a hybrid. The 'Coronation' Class of 'Pacifics' had now been built, and to some extent it resembled them. The same 6 ft 6 in coupled wheels were retained, as were the boiler and cab, but it was given 'Coronation' cylinders and motion, new frames, a new superheater, a new smokebox and a single chimney. As rebuilt, and turned out in British Railways green livery, with the lion-and-wheel emblem on the tender, the BR number 46202 on the cab sides, and the name of the Queen's daughter, *Princess Anne*, above the front coupled wheels, it had an imposing appearance and appeared set for a new lease of life. On 15 August 1952 it was sent to Crewe to begin service on express trains.

Fate had something else in store. On 8 October, less than seven weeks later, the up sleeping car express from Perth inexplicably passed three signals which were at danger and ran at 60 miles an hour into the back of a crowded commuter train which was standing at the platform in Harrow and Wealdstone station. The last three coaches of the commuter train were telescoped into one, with very great loss of life, and the 'Pacific' at the head of the colliding train, whose crew were also killed, left the rails and fouled the down fast line; meanwhile, the 8 am morning express to Liverpool, double-headed with 'Jubilee' No 45637 *Windward Islands* piloting No 46202 was rapidly approaching in the

opposite direction, somewhat before time because of the extra provision of locomotive power, and already accepted by the Harrow signalman. (Had the pilot, which was returning to its home shed and merely attached to the front of the train for the sake of convenience, not been there, the further accident would probably have been avoided, since the down train would then have been at least a mile nearer to London and would have run into adverse signals). The Liverpool train struck the derailed 'Pacific' head on; both its locomotives were thrown leftwards across the station platforms and were so severely damaged that they had to be scrapped. So the rebuilt 'turbomotive' never had a chance to show what it could do. All that remain of it are a few photographs.

No longer turbine-driven, named Princess Anne *and in British Railways green livery, No 46202 is posed for an official photograph. Less than two months later it was involved in the Harrow accident and had to be scrapped. (NRM)*

19

Bulleid's 'Q1' freight locomotives

As the Contents page indicates, one particular locomotive engineer, O.V.S. Bulleid, receives the lion's share of mention in this book. Indeed, his share could well have been larger, had one chosen to include his 'Merchant Navy' and 'West Country' 'Pacifics' as a further example of experiments with steam, for there was much that was experimental about them. However, these engines have had so many books devoted to them that it seems best to leave well alone, and Mr Bulleid is accordingly offered here as a three-course lunch rather than as a four-course dinner.

He was a remarkable man, about whom many stories have been told. He ended his career in the Irish Republic, and it would have been fitting had he been an Irishman, but in fact he was born in New Zealand of British parentage, and returned to this country for his education, which included not only secondary school training but also spells at Universities. Most of his working life was spent on the Great Northern Railway before and after it was merged in the LNER, with a short interlude during his latter twenties as Assistant Works Manager and Chief Draughtsman at the French Westinghouse Company's works in Paris, during which period he married the youngest daughter of the Great Northern Locomotive Superintendent, H.A. Ivatt. Back in Doncaster again in 1911, at the age of 29, he began an association with H.N. Gresley which did not end till 1937, when he accepted the top locomotive job on the Southern Railway. As Gresley's Personal Assistant he has associated with him in designing such celebrated engines as the 'A1', 'A3' and 'A4' 'Pacifics', the six 2-8-2s intended for the Edinburgh–Aberdeen line and the high-pressure 4-6-4 No 10000, described above.

Among those who knew him his brilliance and ingenuity became something of a byword. Ideas came to him as readily as quips to a comedian — and indeed there was just a touch of the latter about him. When on the LNER he once observed to his colleague, A.H. Peppercorn, Gresley's next-but-one successor as Chief Mechanical Engineer, 'Pep, if you design a locomotive with five driving wheels your name is made'. Nothing, it seems, was too bizarre to be contemplated, though when it came to putting ideas into practice common sense usually prevailed. It was obvious, however, that when he came to design his own engines he would not be retrained by convention.

Invited in the spring of 1937 to apply for the post of Chief Mechanical Engineer on the Southern Railway, in place of R.E.L. Maunsell who was due to retire early due to ill-health, he complied and was appointed. Once Maunsell had gone he set about assessing the quantity and state of the locomotive stock. The Southern Railway was destined for progressive electrification and money for new steam locomotives was hard to come by, but Bulleid exercised his considerable powers of persuasion and got the Board to agree to a modernization programme, partly of rebuilding existing engines and partly of new construction. He regarded the 'King Arthurs' as too old to be worth altering, but he gave special attention to improving the somewhat unsatisfactorily performing 'Lord Nelsons', giving them new cylinders and Lemaitre-type multiple jet exhausts; their work improved greatly in consequence, though their appearance suffered somewhat. He then began to do the same with the 4-4-0 'Schools', but the alteration did not improve their otherwise excellent performance, so he modified only half of them. At the time when the Second World War broke out he was beginning to work out his plans for new express and freight engines.

Having put the first of his 'Pacifics' on the road in 1941, he turned to the problem of the freight engine shortage. The Southern Railway never did have large flows of goods traffic; in the areas where its lines reached it had only one comparatively small coalfield, in East Kent, and far fewer industrial concerns than can be found there now. It was predominantly a passenger line. However, since the outbreak of the war freight movement by rail had been on the increase all over the country, since movement of material by road required petrol or diesel oil, which was then only to be obtained from abroad in ships which had to run the gauntlet of submarines and enemy aircraft, so both commodities were rationed — severely in the case of private car owners. Railway locomotives and electricity generating stations, however, could be run on coal, of which there was plenty under the ground which did not have to be imported. When Bulleid took over from Maunsell, the Southern definitely did not have enough goods locomotives. The latter had designed one just prior to his retirement, and 20 had been built — the 0-6-0 'Q' Class. They bore a typical Maunsell appearance, being inside cylindered and, above the running plate, resembling his 'E1' and 'L1' 4-4-0 passenger engines. However, they were not particularly powerful and it was found that they did not steam well. Bulleid therefore decided that an improved type of 0-6-0 was needed.

A locomotive was required which would be able to run over as much of the Southern Railway as was possible. The Civil Engineer declared that if the locomotive's weight could be kept down to 54 tons it would be able to traverse over 93 per cent of the system's route mileage. The

20 'Q' Class engines each weighed just over 49 tons, but with a nominal tractive effort of 26,157 lbs they lacked the pulling power that was necessary to cope with contemporary loads. Bulleid had to make a choice; he could either build a rehashed version of the 'Q', making it a little more forceful and using existing standardized parts, or else design an entirely new type, ignoring the convenience of standardization, and going all out to get maximum power with minimum weight. He chose to do the latter.

The first thing to be considered was the boiler, together with the fire-box. Both had to be as large as possible within the constraints of the loading gauge and the need to give the driver a clear view forward. The largest firebox so far designed on the Southern was that incorporated in the 'Lord Nelson' engines. A somewhat shortened version of this, with a grate area of 27 square feet, larger than any other on any existing 0-6-0, was decided on, and time and material were saved through it being possible to use the same press-blocks as had been used for the 'Nelson' firebox. In regard to the boiler, the wheelbase and cylinder positions limited its length to 10 ft 6 in, a little less than in the 'Q', but in width it tapered backwards from 5 ft to 5 ft 9 in, and in fact had a capacity one-sixth as large again. The boiler was pressed to 230 lbs per square inch, as against the 200 lbs of the 'Q'. So, though the cylinders and coupled wheel dimensions remained the same, the tractive effort was nearly 4,000 lbs more.

However, the total weight of the finished engine, in working order, was under 2½ tons greater than that of the 'Q'. This was achieved by ruthlessly removing every piece of metal that was not absolutely necessary. In the first place, the wheels were made ten per cent lighter than the spoked ones on Maunsell's engine by using the special design of cast steel wheel interiors that Bulleid had devised with the collaboration of the Sheffield steel firm of Firth Brown and Company and with which he had already fitted his 'Merchant Navy' 'Pacifics'. Then he cut out unnecessary weight from the framing, replacing castings with fabricated parts wherever possible. Over the boiler, which was lagged with glass fibre, a kind of wrap-around casing was placed, supported by the frame; in section it resembled a horseshoe and was slightly wider than the smokebox exterior. The most astonishing piece of weight-saving, however, to the eyes of those accustomed to traditional locomotive exteriors, was the absence of running plates holding splashers for the wheels. This evoked more criticism than almost anything else — more even than the ugly wide stove-pipe chimney and the canister-like regulator cover (one could scarcely call it a dome). The whole ensemble reminded one of a man who had gone out without putting his trousers on. Drivers and firemen were alarmed in case a coupling rod should break while in motion and they would be struck by fragments from it. However, no such accident ever occurred.

The smokebox also had unusual features. Instead of being made a circular drum, into which the interior contents had to be made to fit, it was, as it were, built around these, so that the sectional shape came out as a flat-topped horseshoe more or less but not quite matching the boiler-wrapping section, and sheared off at the bottom in a straight line, beneath which the front ends and tail rods of the piston valves poked out, looking like owls' eyes. The smokebox door, which was circular, was held in position by eight circumferential clips. The cab was large, made out of thin sheet steel, with a roof from which a flexible fabric continuation extended to meet an endcab at the front of the tender. To meet wartime exigencies, shutters were fitted to the cab sides to hinder light from escaping during the black-out. Almost as much protection was given to the crew as a tank engine cab would have afforded. There was a point in this, as it was intended that the engine should run as readily backwards as forwards. The tenders themselves were similar to those of the 'Pacifics'; they curved out slightly at the sides, held as much coal as those of the 'Q' 0-6-0s and slightly more water.

It was not to be expected that vociferous criticism, publicly and privately expressed, would be lacking, even though it was wartime when much could be forgiven. (After all, no one ever complained that an Army tank was not a seemly object). When shown a photograph of the first 'Q1', Sir William Stanier remarked that he didn't believe it, and on a later occasion enquired where the key was. Traditionalists were aghast. The locomotive designers of former times, it was implied, were

O.V.S. Bulleid's 'Q1' 0-6-0 No C16, on the Southern Railway at Eastleigh in 1946. A minor peculiarity of these locomotives was that the steps to the cab were attached to the tender. (NRM)

turning in their graves. Had that been the case, George Jackson Churchward was probably chuckling as well, remembering how rude some people had been about his own creations. Bulleid was in fact carrying Churchward's principle, that whatever worked best would in the end be found acceptable to the eye, to its logical extreme. In his own words, 'form follows function and function creates form'.

C. Hamilton Ellis, himself an artist and aesthete, who could savour with appreciation both the handsome and the bizarre in a railway locomotive, made comments in an anonymous article in a railway journal which are worth quoting in this context:

'The appearance of the Q1 Class goods engines has been greeted with more extravagant invective than, perhaps, any locomotives to appear on a British railway since the advent of the first Great Western 4-6-0 express engine, No 100, over forty years ago ... Much derision has been aroused, for instance, by the absence of running plates on the Q1 and the consequent complete exposure of the wheels. Now the running plate is a survival of the days when it was common practice, owing to primitive means of lubrication, for the fireman to make somewhat precarious journeys to and from the front end while travelling at speed. It may reasonably be claimed that to a great extent platforms are retained on modern engines for the same reasons as buttons survive on the back of a morning or dress coat — because they have been there for generations and once upon a time served a useful purpose ...

'The contention is preposterous that the Southern Q1 Class should look like an inflated edition of the Stroudley C1 ... Another example of effete aesthetic traditions may be cited in the case of the chimney, as designed for the majority of British locomotives. In the days when, as Mr O.V. Bulleid said some months ago, locomotives had "nice real chimneys", a flared top, whether built up of copper plate, cast separately in iron or cast in one piece with the stack, considerably improved the appearance of locomotives. With the very short chimneys involved in the use of large high-pitched boilers, the flare becomes necessarily redimentary and, more than that, definitely impairs the smokelifting capacity of these chimneys. Where it is retained this is simply done for no better reason than that chimneys have always had flared tops and should therefore continue to have them ... What is needed is a new aesthetic style, suited to the structural peculiarities of the modern engine, and it would appear that Mr Oliver Bulleid has begun to evolve just such a style.'

The 'Q1' had some other novelties not usually found in an 0-6-0 freight engine. A five-nozzled multiple jet exhaust was fitted, like those which had been placed in the rebuilt 'Lord Nelsons'. The utmost care was taken in designing the cylinders and valves to ensure free passage of steam, so that fast running could be achieved when necessary — for it was expected that the 'Q1's would sometimes have to haul semi-fast passenger trains. An air-blower was fitted inside the exhaust cavity, so that when the regulator was shut while the engine was in motion, no vacuum would be formed into which ash might be sucked from the inside of the smokebox. The holes for filling the tender tank were placed not at its rear but at the front, so that there was no need for the fireman to climb up to the top of the coal when water was taken.

Once it had been introduced, the 'Q1' was found to have one fault that occasioned alarm among footplatemen and caused complaints. Its braking power was not commensurate with its hauling ability. When put at the head of a train of wagons which did not have continuous brakes, in certain circumstances stopping could be difficult, such as when descending a gradient. The situation was partly met by fitting heavier rear brakes, but when these were not considered sufficient some continuously braked vehicles were placed between the tender and the train. Bulleid was in fact looking to the future, when he believed all trains, passenger or goods, would be continuously braked (as is now the case) and considered that the railways were dragging their feet in this respect.

Perhaps the most surprising thing about the 'Q1' was its speed capability. Bulleid had designed it to run fast if necessary. From a machine with driving wheels only 5 ft 1 in across, 60-miles-an-hour running was neither required nor expected on any other British railway. Bulleid expected and obtained it. His enginemen were not at first convinced that it was a good idea. To calm their apprehensions, Bulleid organized a demonstration trip between Ashford and Maidstone, with the engine travelling tender first. This line has some very steep gradients. He climbed aboard the tender as the train was about to start, perched himself there and signalled the right-away. The crew had evidently been told to 'give it everything', and as their General was now leading from the front (instead of from well in the rear as was customary in modern armies) the troops followed him enthusiastically. At one point the speed reached 75 miles an hour. (One imagines that this must have been on the descent from Lenham beyond Hollingbourne, which was six miles long and included pitches at 1 in 100. It could scarcely

'Q1' No 33015 (BR numbering) at Ashford, Kent, in 1952. Note the flexible covering between the locomotive cab roof and its counterpart on the tender; also the holes drilled in the framing to reduce weight. (NRM)

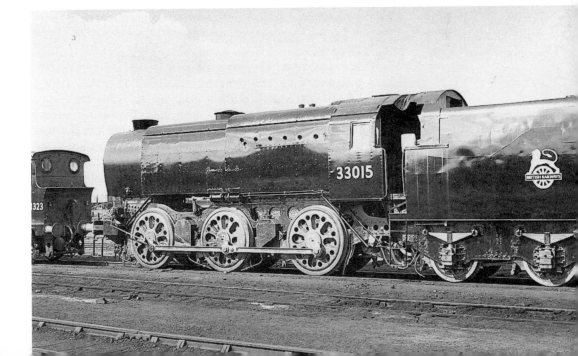

'Q1' Class No C37 at the head of a Feltham-Southampton freight train passing Weybridge. (NRM)

have been further on, where the gradient sharpens to 1 in 60 immediately before the slack for Maidstone). And all this going backwards! Fears were calmed, though it is not recorded that a 'Q1' ever went as fast as that again.

It seems a pity that, with such a turn of speed, and with a power capacity not far short of that of a 'Lord Nelson', these locomotives were never used on express trains. Though the mind may boggle at the thought of one of them heading the 'Golden Arrow', there were many schedules on the Southern Railway, and later on the Southern Region of British Railways, on which time could easily have been kept by brisk uphill running without the necessity to exceed 70 miles an hour anywhere — such as those of the boat trains taking the Chatham or Maidstone routes, with their steep inclinations. Bulleid could with advantage have built more of them and correspondingly fewer 'West Country' and 'Battle of Britain' 'Pacifics'. They would have had to spend less energy hauling their own weight (at least the equivalent of one passenger coach) and would almost certainly have spent less time undergoing repairs. The widespread belief that an engine with five-foot wheels could not achieve high speeds, which he had shown to be unfounded, was to receive further rebuttal in later years when the Class '9' Standard 2–10–0s were occasionally used on express passenger trains — as will be described in the last chapter but one of this book.

The 'Q1's lasted for some 20 years, giving good service and no trouble. They would probably have lasted much longer, but in the late 'fifties the decision was taken to build no new steam locomotives. Soon afterwards the notorious Dr Beeching, who brought the executioner's axe to so many hundreds of miles of railway, in 1963 ordered that no more steam locomotives were to receive major renewals. Soon afterwards No 33028, having broken a cylinder, was towed away to be broken up — sent, as it were, to the mortuary instead of the operating theatre. One by one the others followed suit, except for one which was rescued, restored to its former livery and set to work on the Bluebell Line in Sussex, only 15 miles from its Brighton birthplace, a competent ugly sister amid resplendent older Cinderellas.

'Q1' No 33035 has an easy task with a short freight train bound for Hastings passing through Tonbridge station. (NRM)

20

Bulleid's 'Leader' 0-6-6-0

None of the experimental locomotives mentioned in the foregoing pages raised quite so many eyebrows as the one now to be described. In appearance, and in many of its features, it was completely unconventional. Its designer's intentions cannot be faulted, and if he had had more time in which to carry them out, and a little more trust on the part of those who had the last word, its faults might have been eliminated and it might have established itself as the steam locomotive of the future, able to challenge its diesel-driven rival over much (though certainly not all) of the British Railways system, capable of hauling fast trains as well as slow trains and being independent of turntables. If it could have been developed earlier, and had been able to take part in the Locomotive Exchanges of 1948, it might have influenced the thinking of those members of the British Railways Executive whose business it was to prescribe what the new Standard locomotives should be like. However, circumstances prevented that, for soon after O.V.S. Bulleid became Chief Mechanical Engineer on the Southern Railway the Second World War broke out and lasted for nearly six years; as soon as hostilities had ended the result of a General Election held very quickly afterwards made it plain that the nationalization of the whole railway system, mooted in 1918 and then replaced by the four groupings, would soon become a fact. With nationalization, Bulleid ceased to have the authority he had previously wielded, and soon afterwards he left British Railways and took himself off to the Irish Republic to be Chief Mechanical Engineer of Coras Iompair Eireann, and the 'Leader' type locomotive, lacking the drive of his personality behind it, lapsed instead of leading. Whether the sentence passed upon it by the Railway Executive was murder most foul or justifiable infanticide in still keenly debated in railway circles.

Exactly when Bulleid began to conceive the idea of an 0-6-6-0 steam locomotive, workable from either end, with boiler, firebox, coal and water supply carried on a frame resting on two powered bogies, is not known. Until he had produced the 'Merchant Navy' 'Pacific' Class he had never been the author of a new locomotive; one cannot tell what he may have dreamed about in his more imaginative moments. He came to the Southern Railway at a time when there was a shortage of all kinds of steam locomotives adequate for their tasks, and this was still to some extent the case eight years later, particularly in the shortage of tank locomotives suitable for shunting trains into and out of Waterloo. The small 0-4-4 tanks of Dugald Drummond's design were still in use after 40 years and were hardly up to pulling 13-coach trains of modern stock. The Traffic Manager at Waterloo wanted larger ones — 0-6-4s instead of 0-4-4s would have suited him well enough — but for various reasons Bulleid did not favour this type, and after putting forward plans more or less based on his unconventional 'Q1' freight locomotive (described in the previous chapter), which were turned down, he suggested that a further number of 'Q1's be built, since he felt they would serve just as well as the suggested tank engines and were in any case designed to run backwards. The Traffic Manager did not agree and there was further correspondence over the matter, Bulleid proposing further tank designs, including one with a water tube boiler. This, put forward in February 1946, envisaged an 0-4-4-0. The germ idea of the 'Leader' was now beginning to show up on paper. Like the others it was rejected.

By now his thinking was definitely out of step with that of his more conventionally minded colleagues and fellow railway engineers. He certainly did not consult the former as often as they felt he should. Like Gladstone, who wanted to establish Home Rule in Ireland, he was 'an old man in a hurry' — because Home Rule on the Southern Railway was shortly to end. Six months earlier another old man in a hurry had called a General Election, and lost it. A Labour government committed to nationalizing the railways had been elected. Public ownership of a unified railway system would mean that there would be one Chief Mechanical Engineer, not four, and Bulleid, now well over 60, knew that person would not be himself. His time was short, and this may well have prompted him to get something built in which the ideas he had been nurturing could be exemplified — a sort of *chef-d'oeuvre*, after which he could retire or take up a post elsewhere with some éclat, and not just disappear into obscurity. True, he had constructed his 'Pacifics', the most unconventional express locomotives ever seen on any British line in any numbers since the days of Francis Webb, and very successful they were when in good condition, though a source of exasperated annoyance to those who had to service or repair them. But another unclimbed peak had come into his view and he was determined to scale it if he could. He would build the steam locomotive of the future, one which could successfully compete with the diesel-driven type. Like Tennyson's Ulysses he believed that

'Some work of the noble note may yet be done,
Not unbecoming men who strove with gods ...'

or, in his case, with fellow colleagues.

Two months later he submitted his first plan for an 0-6-6-0, and while it was still being considered by the Board he was already busying himself with improvements upon it. During September, when a meeting of the Rolling Stock Progress Committee was held at Waterloo, he submitted his latest drawings along with a memorandum, of which part is quoted below:

> 'LEADING CLASS; SHUNTING ENGINE: C-C TYPE
>
> The principal features of the new engine are as follows:
> 'This design of engine makes full and complete use of the total weight for adhesive purposes and braking ... The whole of the moving parts will be enclosed and fitted with automatic lubrication, so that it will not be necessary for the driver to lubricate any part of the machine. Each engine will have three "simple" cylinders driving the intermediate axle [of each bogie]. The load is transmitted to the leading and trailing axles by chain drive in an oiltight casing. The [roller bearing] axleboxes will be contained in an oilbath ... The leading engine will exhaust to atmosphere by way of the blast pipe in the smokebox so as to provide the necessary draught in the boiler, but exhaust from the trailing engine will be used to heat the water in the tank ... The boiler is a new design which will obviate the maintenance inherent in the normal type of locomotive boiler. The engine will also be fitted with feed water treatment incorporated in the tender. The controls of the engine will be such that both men will be able to carry out their duties seated ... so that they can drive in either direction ... By condensing steam from one engine the water consumption should be appreciably reduced. The engine is fitted with 5 ft 1 in wheels, and this in conjunction with the short stroke will allow the engine to run at speeds up to 90 mph without exceeding the normal piston speed ... The front end will be based on that successfully introduced in the "West Country" Class engines in order to ensure that the steam, when the engine is working lightly, is carried clear of the cab.'

One or two comments on the above should be made here. Firstly, the appellation 'Shunting Engine' is an understatement of the engine's intended scope. It would perform such duties efficiently, of course, but not at the envisaged 90 miles an hour! It was clearly a general-purpose locomotive. Secondly, in referring to an 'oil bath' and an 'oiltight casing' he was inviting challenge, since on the 'Merchant Navy' and the 'West Country' locomotives the oilbaths had leaked and given continual trouble; however, no one reading this memorandum seems to have taken him up on this. Thirdly, one wonders why he said that both members of the crew would be able to carry out their duties seated. How would the fireman do this? Nothing is said about using an automatic stoker. Possibly Bulleid was thinking in terms of oil-burning. If so, he did not spell it out.

He was expecting to be asked to build 25 as that was the number of new shunting tank engines the Traffic Department had in mind. After a good deal of argument among members of the Rolling Stock Committee he was told he might build five. This was not going to be much help to the Traffic Department, who wanted all the Drummond 'M7's replaced as quickly as possible, but they gave Bulleid his opportunity and he set all the wheels in motion. In October 1946 he told the Board that one of the new engines would be ready the following June and that the other four would follow as quickly as possible. At this point the Traffic Manager made a suggestion which was accepted, and which was perhaps critical in ensuring that the 'Leader' project never came to fruition. He asked that the five engines should be coal-fired, not oil-fired, to ensure greater mobility. The Attlee Government had already entered into a commitment to allow oil fuel on railway locomotives, but evidently doubts were entertained that it would always be available.

Bulleid's expectation that the locomotive would be ready in June 1947 was much too sanguine. Actual construction was so much delayed that it did not start until July of that year. It was assembled at Brighton works, where Bulleid had his head office and was able to keep in constant touch with the project. Construction proceeded slowly, and it was not until the following May that the first complete frame was ready. By this time the Southern Railway no longer existed, having become the Southern Region of British Railways, and the chief power in the land was the Railway Executive. Sir Eustace Missenden, who had been the Chairman of the Southern, chaired the Executive, and he was sympathetic towards Bulleid. However, the new Chief Mechanical Engineer of British Railways, R.A. Riddles, was much more wary. Bulleid was now one of his close colleagues, and no longer king of his locomotive department as heretofore, but a mere proconsul. So a recommendation from Waterloo in November 1947 that a further 31 of the new engines be authorized was not endorsed by the Railway Executive. The latter's members were becoming worried about the mounting cost of the project. It appeared that the five engines whose building was already in progress were going to cost twice as much as five similarly powered locomotives of conventional design. The experiment had been allowed to get under way, but authority's attitude had altered, and the tilt was towards disapproval. Riddles had his own ideas about what British Railways needed in the way of steam locomotives, and these eventually bore fruit in the Standard designs. In relation to these Bulleid's engines would be mavericks. He was lucky to be allowed to continue building them.

When it finally emerged from Brighton works on 21 June 1949, No 36001 (the number allotted to it by British Railways) could very well have been mistaken by a casual onlooker, first for an electric locomotive of a new design, and then, when the absence of pick-up shoes was noticed, for a diesel locomotive — though once it was on the move its exhaust would have given it away. Everything above the frames was enclosed, the middle third of each side of the covering extending downwards in a shallow curve. On the right-hand side there was a door at either end giving access, at the top of a ladder made of iron bars, to the front or rear driving compartment; on the left-hand side the sweep of the side sheets was broken by a door for the fireman, also at the top

No 36001, the first (and only) Bulleid 'Leader' 0-6-6-0 to be completed, leaving Brighton with a test train. Note the covers for the chains which served instead of coupling rods. (NRM)

of a bar-ladder, with a small window beside it, about two-thirds of the way from the front. The two six-wheel bogies each had casings hiding the chains running on sprockets which, on the right of the engine, linked the central and front axles and, on the left, the central and rear; in this way coupling rods were made unnecessary and hammer-blow on the track reduced. The two ends of the locomotive resembled each other, having three forward-facing windows, the side ones slanting very slightly backwards. Seen from the side, the roof-line dipped down forward from the rear cab for several feet; this was where the tender tank was filled and coal supplies replenished. At either end of the locomotive there was a considerable vertical gap between the cab floor and the buffer beam. The whole engine was painted grey over a black undercoat, and lined out in panels with black and red. It will be noted that Bulleid's statement that the front end would be similar to that of a 'West Country' Class engine in order to make sure that the steam would be carried clear of the cab was not fulfilled — for the obvious reason that the cabs were at either end, so that, however much steam might be drifting, it could not obscure the driver's vision.

So much for the external appearance; now to consider what was out of sight. Within the outer casing, at the front end, behind the cab, were the smokebox and boiler, which were more or less the same as those used on the 'West Country' Class 'Pacifics', and these supplied superheated steam at 280 lbs per square inch through flexible piping to the cylinders in both bogies. Unusually, and some might think perversely, the boiler was not placed centrally but offset six inches to the right of the centre line; this was to leave room for a corridor joining the two driving cabs so that the fireman could communicate with the driver when necessary. This was the most criticized feature of the whole design, and it is to be noted that when Bulleid repeated his 0–6–6–0 experiment in Ireland he placed the boiler along the centre line and the cabs on either side. Despite some attempts at weighting the left-hand side of the engine, the centre of gravity of the whole machine remained to the right of the mid-line. The firebox was dry-sided (ie there was no water either side of it continuous with the water above the crown) and the dry sides were lined with firebricks which interlocked with each other like the pieces of a jigsaw puzzle. It incorporated two thermic syphons by means of which boiler water circulated from the rear lower end of the boiler through the furnace itself to the firebox crown. The stays across the flat sides of the siphons were tubular so that the firebox gases could penetrate from either side and increase the amount of heat transference. The fire door was placed obliquely across the left-hand corner of the firebox. Both the latter and the boiler were welded throughout.

The two powered six-wheeled bogies had some unusual features. To begin with, almost every component was welded from steel plates, sheets, tubes or bars, cut or machined. The inside cylinders, three in each bogie, 12 in by 15 in, drove cranks inclined at 120 degrees on the central axle. A modified form of Walschaerts valve gear, similar to that used in the 'Merchant Navy' and 'West Country' 'Pacifics', worked from a separate axle driven by a chain from the central wheel-axle, and was

'Leader' Class boilers under construction at Brighton. (NRM)

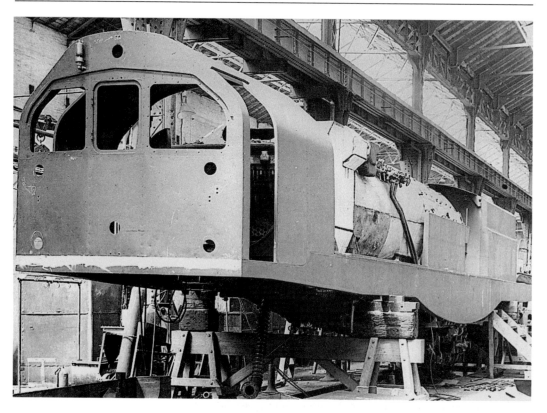

'Leader' Class locomotive under construction, with the boiler being fitted to the frame. (NRM)

enclosed in an oilbath. As in the Paget locomotive described above in Chapter 12, steam admission was through sleeve valves which lined the interiors of the cylinders and partially revolved from one side to the other and back again inside them. To try out this type of valve Bulleid fitted an old Marsh 'Atlantic', *Hartland Point*, with them; tests made with it lasted on and off for a year and a half, and despite one or two untoward incidents and one serious accident when a valve sleeve broke into three pieces, he considered that the method had proved itself. The exhaust steam from the front bogie was expelled through the blast pipe and chimney to the atmosphere in the usual way, to provide the smokebox draught. From the rear bogie it went to a condenser and warmed the water in the tank. Each bogie had four flat bearing surfaces, well supplied with oil, on which the main frame of the locomotive body rested, so that no central pivot was necessary. The bogie wheels were of the same pressed steel type as were used in the 'Pacifics' and 'Q1's, and each was of 5 ft 1 in diameter.

Two other innovations were modifications to the springing of the wheels and the braking system. The wheels' springs were of the conventional leaf type, but each one on either side had an oil-filled drum which acted as a damper-out of vertical movement within the axlebox horns. A similar device was later used in some British Railways coach bogies, though it is not certain whether the example of the 'Leader' was being consciously adopted. The brakes were of the vacuum type, but whereas in other locomotives these usually relied on a single vacuum cylinder, each of the bogies of the 'Leader' had two such cylinders, and there were others above them in the main body of the engine which (if one may so describe it) stored additional vacuum, and when the negative pressure went below a certain figure the air ejectors began to work automatically. So the driver always had an adequate vacuum at his disposal.

It would take up too much space to describe in detail the other unusual features of the locomotive; here they are simply given a mention. Oil pumps driven by a small steam turbine kept the flood-lubricating oil around the motion in movement. A hopper ash-pan below the large rocking firegrate was designed to discharge directly downwards into a reception pit when it had to be emptied. The coal bunker was of triangular section and opened below into a channel from which coal could be shovelled. The main water tank in the tender, warmed by exhaust steam which condensed within it, had cross-plates to reduce surging. An additional pair of tanks within the outer sheeting of the engine slightly increased the water supply and to some extent added weight to the left-hand side to compensate (though not sufficiently) for the off-setting of the boiler. The fireman when at work faced inwards, not forwards, shovelling his coal from a chute to his right and through the fire-hole to his left. At either end the driver's cab was so arranged that all the controls were within his reach as he sat in a padded seat on the left of his cab.

Once construction had been completed, testing began in a long series of out-and-home journeys from Brighton, at first nearly always running light, but from September 1949 onwards mostly with a load, which

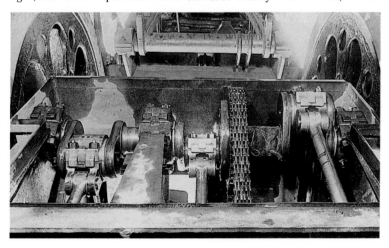

The crank axle of a 'Leader' bogie, showing the chain which worked the valve gear axle. (NRM)

varied between 150 and 255 tons. Two loaded runs were planned early in September between Brighton and Victoria, but both failed to reach London because the engine ran short of steam and could not get further than half-way. The test runs were not made on the busy main line, but between Brighton and Polegate, Crowborough, Oxted or Tunbridge Wells over secondary routes, some of which have now been closed. Of 70 out-and-back journeys, 33 were classed as failures, something having gone wrong with the engine, most commonly in one of the powered bogies. Firebricks also tended to become dislodged, and on one occasion so many fell away that the metal side of the firebox became red hot and firing became impossible. On 18 August a run was made to Eastleigh and back in order to weigh the engine; to the general consternation it proved to be more than 20 tons over its official figure of 110 tons. On October a sleeve valve broke and had to be replaced. But then things began to look brighter. Twenty-four test runs, all with loads, made between 2 November and 16 December, produced only five small faults which were quickly repaired. It looked as if the teething troubles were coming to an end. But any congratulations were premature.

Bulleid had himself resigned from British Railways in September 1949 and gone to Ireland, to become Chief Mechanical Engineer at Inchicore works on the CIE. What now happened to the engine depended on the decision of the Railway Executive, and this in turn depended on whether the man responsible for the whole of British Railways' stock of locomotives, R.A. Riddles, gave it the thumbs-up or thumbs-down. Riddles had never been sympathetic to Bulleid's conception of a general-purpose 0-6-6-0, but as its construction had gone so far before nationalization actually began, he had allowed it to be completed and the building of the four others to be begun. Soon after Bulleid had departed for Ireland he gave orders that further work on these other four was to be discontinued for the moment, though one of them was only two days from completion. It also seems likely that the long holiday from testing which the prototype was now given — from mid-December 1949 to mid-June 1950 — was because of rumours that had reached his ears that this overweight and imperfectly-balanced engine was damaging the track. (In fact, this does not appear to have been the case). In March 1950 he made a report to the Railway Executive, giving his own opinion about the engine. He said he was proposing to resume trial runs as soon as the faulty weight distribution had been corrected, and that these would include dynamometer car tests with suitable loads. If these tests revealed that the 'Leader' could do its work using substantially less water and coal for each unit of work done, he would consider authorizing further modifications in the hope that its designer's expectations might then be fulfilled. His report seemed to some members of the Executive not drastic enough; they would have preferred stopping work on the project altogether. Riddles, however, was prepared to give it another opportunity to prove itself.

So on 13 April 1950, the 'Leader' took itself under its own steam from Brighton to Eastleigh, having had at the former place some further modifications which much improved its riding performance. At Eastleigh they did what they could to improve the engine's balance by adding weights in the side-corridor at floor level, and putting in transverse struts weighted with old brake-blocks, firebars and pieces of pig-iron. Eventually it was considered acceptably balanced, at the cost of being made heavier still. Orders were given that the locomotive was not to be used on any track not already cleared for the 'Merchant Navy' engines and a limit of 50 miles an hour was imposed. Trials first began in a small way, along the short stretch between Eastleigh and Fratton, and the question of unwillingness on the part of enginemen had to be solved. Its reputation had preceded it to Eastleigh, as a locomotive which, however pleasant for its driver, nearly cooked its fireman. Eventually two volunteers were found, but these both insisted that they would only work the engine bunker-first, since that was the cooler end. So the tests could only be made when Driver Smith and Fireman Talbot were both available.

The full-scale trials took place on the main Bournemouth to London line, between Eastleigh and Woking, generally with more substantial loads than during the previous year and, after the first two, with the dynamometer car between the engine and the train. Something like the previous experience was, on the whole, repeated — a sequence of runs marred by accidents being followed by a number without any. On 12 June the engine would not steam properly; later it was found that the smokebox door had not been properly shut! Three days later poor steaming was again experienced, and it was necessary to halt for a while until pressure was recovered. On 29 June, with the dynamometer car attached, strange noises were heard as it started, which turned at Winchester into a loud bang each time the wheels revolved. Taken back gently down the hill to Eastleigh and examined there, the 'Leader' was found to have snapped one of its crank axles. This, everyone supposed, was surely the end. Riddles, however, insisted that it should be repaired and the tests continued. So both crank axles were renewed, replacements being had from Brighton which had been intended for one of the other four engines whose building had been halted, and after two months' delay the trials were again resumed. The engine still seemed to have a jinx on it; there was difficulty in maintaining the boiler pressure, the mechanical lubrication would not work properly, coal and water consumptions were unduly high and cinders were thrown through the chimney. The valves did not function properly. So another spell of attention was needed and another month's delay experienced.

Back on the road on 25 September, the engine now behaved itself well during four trials during the following four days. Nothing went wrong, booked time was kept and the words 'a good performance' appeared in the reports made. On the return to Eastleigh during the last trial the engine was given its head during the descent from Litchfield and the stipulated limit of 50 miles an hour was greatly exceeded, though unfortunately no one has ever disclosed what the maximum was. The 'Leader' seemed to have earned a full pardon. However, there was a feeling at Headquarters that it should be tested once more with a load more like the maximum for which it had been designed. So, on 17 October the last trial but one was staged, and this time a member of the Railway Executive, Mr R. Bond, was in the train to observe. After making an impressively effortless start from Eastleigh, when halted at Basingstoke to take water it refused to start in order to draw up to the water column; if not a calamity, this was certainly a fault. On the final trial the load was as much as 480 tons. This was taken up the long rise to Worting Junction at a steady 50, which was almost up to 'Pacific' standards. But at Basingstoke the jinx again manifested itself. The smokebox door had been left very slightly ajar, and cinders and unburnt soot had come through and seemed about to set light to the floor and lagging; the door, too, had become warped. So the train was left behind at Basingstoke, and the engine returned light to Eastleigh. As if to make up for what had happened, it reached a high speed on the descent and rode as smoothly as a passenger coach. A new smokebox could have been found from Brighton if it had been wished. But in fact the 'Leader' never steamed again.

At the end of November, Riddles made a full report of the trials to the Railway Executive. His conclusions amounted to this, that the engine had either to be considerably modified, or else, with its uncompleted fellows at Brighton, scrapped altogether. A very large amount of money had already been spent in building and testing. A great deal more would certainly have to be spent before the type could be put into revenue-earning service. Even if this were to be done, 'the locomotive, as modified, would offer no advantages compared with one of conventional, well-tried design'. So scrapping it had to be.

One cannot blame him; one has to remember the circumstances. That steam traction on British Railways would eventually give place to electric and diesel haulage was now accepted; there would be a period during which steam would still be used, and designs for new Standard locomotives designed to do all that had to be done, from express haulage downwards, were in preparation and some of the engines were being built. Where was the point in building five non-standard mavericks? They would always cost more to repair or maintain, special replacements being needed which would have to be specially made. British Railways had to pay its way and could not afford to indulge in sentiment. One has to agree. But what a pity No 36001 was not preserved and eventually sent to the Railway Museum at York!

21

Bulleid's turf-burner

Ireland, differing from Great Britain in so many other respects, differs also in having almost no coal-mines. (There is in fact one coalfield near Kilkenny, but it produces only about 200,000 tons yearly, of mediocre quality). It has always relied on Great Britain for its supplies of coal, and Irish railways, while they relied on steam traction, had perforce to use British coal, though by the time they received it it was not in good usable condition very often, since it had been handled so much *en route*, being twice loaded into and out of wagons and once into and out of a ship's hold; such treatment was calculated to reduce a great deal of it to slack.

However, Ireland does have an indigenous fuel — peat, which can be dug from the ubiquitous Irish bogs, and which was widely used in domestic fireplaces, especially in the more remote parts. Turf has certain advantages as a fuel; it produces no clinker when burned, and very little ash. However, it is bulky. In terms of ability to produce heat, four times as much in bulk is needed, and over twice as much in weight, as with coal. But since it was to be had locally, in enormous quantities, without any deep mining being necessary, it is not surprising that on two railways attempts were made to use it during the nineteenth century, though these were not persevered with.

The outbreak of the Second World War in 1939 resulted in coal imports from Great Britain being severely restricted; the exigencies of the war effort required it to be used here, and only the poorest quality was sent to Ireland. Since the railway system depended almost entirely on steam locomotives, it was now urgent to find a way of using turf if this was at all possible. The Great Northern Railway, whose system stretched from Dublin as far as Belfast and Londonderry and so was only partly in the Republic, most of its lines being in Ulster, was perhaps better placed to obtain what coal was to be had from Great Britain, but nevertheless decided to experiment with turf, setting aside a 4–4–2 tank engine with which to experiment. It was discovered that combustion tended to be incomplete, that steam pressure could not be maintained, that it was necessary to have a thin fire over the firegrate, and that turf tended to fall too readily through the bars. It was also difficult, in a bunker designed to hold coal, to carry a sufficient supply of turves. When coal-slack was mixed with the turves, however, a better fire was achieved, and for a while this sort of fuel proved fairly successful, but towards the end of the war the coal received from Britain became even worse in quality than before, so briquettes made of turf were substituted and *faute de mieux* the Great Northern managed to run its much reduced services with these.

The Great Southern Railway (which included all the former Irish companies other than the Great Northern) also used turf during the war, and on some branches in the west of Ireland used nothing else. Naturally its services suffered. The writer has in his possession some typed memoirs of an Irish lady who during 1941–44 had frequent cause to travel between Cork and Dublin in order to convey official documents. Before the war she could have done the double journey in a day and still had plenty of time to do what she had to do in Dublin. As things were it took all day to do the 165 miles, since so many stops had to be made to reload the engine's tender with turf. So each business trip took at least twice as long.

After the Republic's railway system had been brought under public ownership under Coras Iompair Eireann, another fuel crisis supervened in the earlier months of 1947, contemporaneously with a coal shortage in Great Britain, and for some months it was only possible to run a skeleton freight service. A Committee was appointed by the Irish Government to report on the parlous transport situation, and it had for one of its technical advisors O.V.S. Bulleid, who was still on what had been the Southern Railway in England but which was now, since January 1948, the Southern Region of British Railways. The possibilities of a turf-burning locomotive now presented themselves to him. As mentioned in the previous chapter, he resigned from British Railways in September 1949 and was appointed as Chief Mechanical Engineer on CIE. He brought with him not only a lifetime's experience of locomotive and railway vehicle manufacture, but also an idea which he thought might be applicable in Ireland — an engine whose design was based on that of the 'Leader' 0-6-6-0 which was then undergoing trials at Brighton, but adapted for burning turf.

It was obvious to those in charge of the Irish railways that reliance on British coal could not go on for ever. They had either to use turf or import oil to be used either in steam or in diesel locomotives. Electrification was not an open option since the traffic on Irish railways was not sufficient to warrant the expense of its introduction. Importing oil meant bringing it from the Middle East (the existence of huge reserves of natural oil and gas under the North Sea not yet being known). Turf was ready to hand in large quantities, and was already being burned in electricity power stations with success. It was possible to site these in close proximity to turf bogs (of which Ireland has many); the input of fuel and the output of electricity could be continuous and constant, the disposition of machinery was not limited by loading gauge requirements and there was no excessive vibration to make the fuel disintegrate into fragments before it was fed into the furnaces. With a locomotive, on the other hand, there would be much vibration, the input and output would vary, it would be difficult to carry much fuel because of the loading gauge, and the fuel itself would have to be transported to places convenient for loading the locomotive — which in effect meant lorry transport. However, the fact that the peat was *there*, not thousands of miles away, stimulated the ever-ingenious Bulleid first to experiment with an existing locomotive and then to design and build one tailored to the burning of turf.

Soon after he arrived at Inchicore he began experimenting. He took an ancient 2–6–0 locomotive, built in 1903, and fitted a pair of pre-heating drums to either side of the existing steam boiler; he also adapted the firebox to take a mechanical stoker. The exhaust system was altered so that instead of being expelled through the blast pipe and chimney, the hot gases from the firebox and the exhausted steam passed through tubes warming the water in the preheaters and the tender before escaping to the atmosphere through a chimney at the rear of the latter. Thus there was no exhaust-induced draught in the smokebox, but a forced draught was instead created from an air-blower mounted on a truck behind the tender, which was driven by a diesel engine of the type used on buses. However, the chimney and smokebox had to be retained for lighting-up purposes. A new tender was attached to the engine, adapted from one that had originally been fitted to a now redundant Midland & Great Western engine; its sides were built up as far as the loading gauge allowed so that as much peat could be carried as possible.

From an aesthetic point of view the appearance of the altered locomotive was pretty ghastly, despite being specially liveried in aluminium paint and lettered EXPERIMENTAL TURF BURNING LOCOMOTIVE. However, one does not worry about what a guinea-pig looks like; the important thing was whether it would work. It was ready early in 1952, and steaming trials followed which lasted for more than a year. In 1954 it was tried out in service on the main line between Dublin and Cork. After making a few journeys it refused one day to start at all, so it was towed back to Inchicore, never to run again. Its importance had been in the data it provided for Bulleid to design its tailor made successor.

The 'Leader' was of course very much in Bulleid's mind when he and his staff prepared the designs, but it was not by any means an exact copy. As with the Southern engine, boiler, firebox and fuel storage tanks were on a single long frame which ran on two six-wheeled powered bogies. However, each bogie had two, not three cylinders, and had piston valves instead of sleeve valves, which were positioned between the cylinders and next to one another. (Bulleid now had the advantage of a rail gauge of 5 ft 3 in, 6½ inches wider than the standard gauge in Great Britain). The coupled wheels were a foot and a half less wide than those of the 'Leader', being only 3 ft 7 in across. (No 90 mph speeds were expected in Ireland!). The cylinders were only 12 in by 14 in, and as

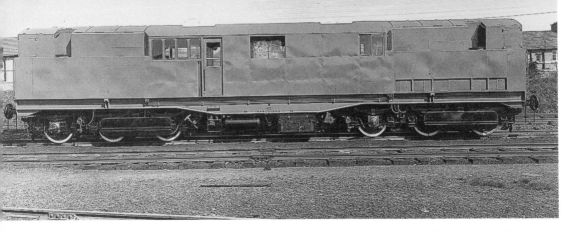

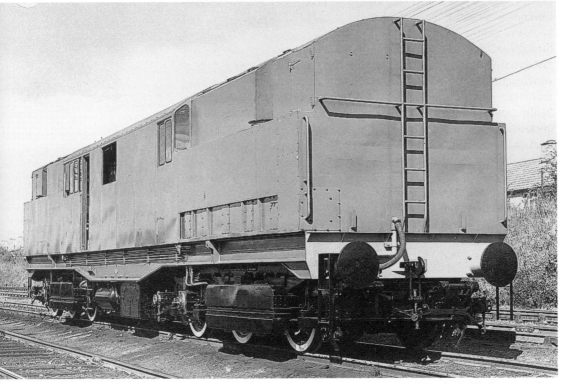

with the 'Leader' the connecting rods were very short. A notable difference from what was usual in other locomotives was that there was no crosshead working in sliding guides attaching each piston rod to the connecting rod, but instead the former carried a second piston which went to and fro sliding inside a tube. There were no oilbaths enclosing any of the moving parts. Wheel-coupling was achieved by external chains covered by casings, as with the 'Leader'. A modified form of Walschaerts valve gear was used.

Seen from either side the upper part of the locomotive looked almost bilaterally symmetrical, except that each driving compartment had only one door, to the driver's left. These compartments were not, as in the

'Leader', at the extreme ends of the engine but at either end of the firebox and boiler, which were central. The driver's lookout was along the left of the narrowed top of the container which, at either end, held both water and turf supplies. The boiler was double, longitudinally placed on either side of a central firebox, both being joined at the top by a wide equalizing pipe so that the pressure was the same in each. Both were also very short, being only 4 feet from end to end; each one had 720 fire tubes of 1 inch diameter. The total heating surface with 1,621 square feet. The central firebox, 6 feet from end to end between the boilers, had a grate area of 22 square feet, and was fed with turves through mechanical stokers at either end, which were under the fireman's control. Steam at 250 lbs per square inch pressure passed through each of the twin regulators, which worked together, into a space just ahead of the boiler at either end, and was there superheated in tubes which zigzagged in the space where the gases from the fire tubes met. It then passed across the top of the driving cab at either end, and was fed to the bogies through flexible tubing. After leaving the cylinders it passed through the pre-heaters at the base of each water tank and was then exhausted upwards through a narrow pipe.

The firebox was not served manually with fuel, but turves were extracted from the lower parts of the turf containers by means of screws whose revolution was under the control of the fireman — the action being somewhat similar to that of the domestic meat-mincing machine, except that the turves did not pass through mincers! They were drawn

The locomotive seen at Inchicore. Note the covers for the chains which linked the outside wheels, similar to those of the 'Leader'. (NRM)

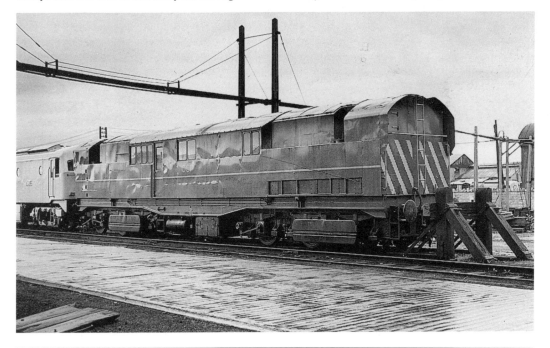

A closer view of the 'turf-burner' showing the number of the locomotive (descriptive of the wheel arrangement), the end ladder giving access to the top of the water tank (covered in this instance to prevent unauthorized access?) and the openings which served as handholds and footholds enabling access to the hinged covers over the tank and bunker; these were duplicated at the other end. (Deegan Photo, Dublin)

through the tubes of the first set of screws to fall into receptacles under the cab floors; other screws then propelled them into the firebox itself, a little above the level of the fire. The fireman's duties were thus not so much physically as mentally demanding; he had to decide when to set the screws in motion, and when to stop them from revolving, according to his estimate of when the furnace needed replenishing, which meant careful inspection of the level of the bed of burning turves as well as consideration of what the boilers were demanding. The hot gases from the firebox, after passing through to the superheater spaces, were then sucked through the pre-heaters at the bottom of the water tanks by turbine-operated fans which thus provided a dual draught on the fire from each end of the locomotive; they then escaped to the atmosphere. Consequently there was almost no audible exhaust — just a gentle hiss from the chimneys. When the boiler was filled, water from the tanks was forced by pumps first through the pre-heaters and then through strainers and clack valves high up on either side near the firebox; a balance pipe connected the two pumps. If necessary the pre-heater could be bypassed and water fed directly to the boiler through other clack valves lower down.

When he designed this locomotive, Bulleid was not thinking merely of producing a turf-burner. It had been made so as to be easily convertible to oil-burning, and suitable equipment had been designed to replace the screw-feed mechanisms and other devices needed with turves. However, this never happened and the equipment was never constructed, CIE went over instead to the use of imported diesel locomotives — as ugly as they were efficient — as did Great Britain, though here the locomotives were much more easy on the eye.

The trials undergone by 'CC1', as it was numbered, appear to have gone much more smoothly, and been much less extensive, than were those of the 'Leader'. It was first steamed in Inchicore works yard in August 1957, and then taken out on to the main line for tests, first light and then with a train. On 4 October it worked a five-coach test train from Dublin to Cork, and then back as far as Portarlington, using the equivalent on a single load of turf — ie 12 tons for the 290-odd miles, or about 92 lbs per mile. Since the calorific value of turf is less than half that of coal, this was not at all bad, and suggested that the Dublin–Cork run could be accomplished with one, or at the most two, stops for taking water. Some problems were experienced with the emission of sparks from the chimneys — on one occasion one of the coaches in the train was set alight — so spark arrestors were fitted inside the chimneys. Another difficulty was that foreign objects in the turf supply sometimes caused the screw-mechanisms to jam. But these were minor matters, easily obviated. The locomotive had virtues to be set against these shortcomings. It easily maintained its designated maximum speed of 70 miles an hour, despite the driving wheels being so small — they would then be turning at over 13 times a second. It was so quiet in running that it could not be heard approaching until it was very close to the hearer, so the driver had to give clear and timely blasts on the whistle. It was also discovered that the fan-draught was extremely effective in raising steam quickly after heavy demands had depleted the boiler.

During its trials between Dublin and Cork it ran some 1,800 miles. It was to run only 200 more before being withdrawn. This seems

The 'turf-burner' under construction at Inchicore. (B. Connel Esq)

surprising, but the failure to use it in regular service (it never hauled a single fare-paying passenger) or to multiply its numbers was probably due to Bulleid's absence from the scene. He retired in May 1958. He was then 75 and had had a long innings so far as tenure of top locomotive supervision posts was concerned — 21 years altogether, first on the Southern and then on CIE. At the time of his retirement the Institute of Locomotive Engineers and the Institute of Transport held a joint summer gathering at Dublin, and four historic locomotives were paraded for their inspection — the ancient Bury single of 1847 which is now on show in the passenger concourse at Cork station, an 0-6-0 built in 1880, the great 4-6-0 *Maeve*, No 800 of the Great Southern, which had done such magnificent running on the mail trains between Dublin and Cork just before the war, and CC1, newly painted in green and fitted with smoke deflectors.

R.A. Riddles, the Chief Mechanical Engineer of British Railways, must have been there; it seems, to judge by his later remarks, that CC1 did not much impress him. In an interview many years later he remarked, 'The suprise to me was that, having failed on the Southern, he went to Ireland and failed there too'. This seems rather unfair. On the evidence we have, the turf-burner does not seem to have been a failure at all, except in not quite fitting into CIE's scheme of things when the decision was made to go over to diesel traction. On the face of it, it would seem that if more had been built they would have given a good account of themselves. At one time CIE did plan to build 50 which could be used additionally to their diesel fleet for seasonal traffic, and act as a reserve of locomotive power if supplies of oil were ever cut off. It may be, of course, that there were problems about CC1 which have never been publicized. Anyhow, the proposal was shelved. The locomotive ran occasionally on goods trains and clocked up a further 200 miles shuttling between Kingsbridge (the present Heuston) and North Wall sidings, before being retired to Inchicore. The company had now lost interest in it, and in 1965 it was scrapped.

22

The Crosti boiler and Giesl ejector experiments on BR

As already mentioned, R.A. Riddles, while Bulleid was building his controversial 'Leader' at Brighton, was himself with his staff designing and beginning to construct a range of standard locomotives which were to be steam's last word in Great Britain before diesel and electric traction replaced it. The production and performance of these locomotives form a last and by no means inglorious chapter in the whole history of British steam. Though they were not built to look beautiful, all but ten (the 'Clan' Class 4-6-2s) can be reckoned as successful, and every rail enthusiast knows what the Class '7' 'Britannias' did on the former Great Eastern and other main lines, redeeming what some considered a certain gauntness of appearance by sparkling performances on accelerated trains.

The last of the standard classes to appear, the Class '9' 2-10-0s, were in some ways the best of all, and the most thermally efficient locomotives ever to have run on British rails. Unprepossessing in appearance almost to the point of appearing misshapen — and beyond that point in one of the two deviations from the norm about to be described — they could, despite their small wheels, go almost anywhere and do almost anything. Designed for heavy freight work, when called on to haul express passenger trains they almost equalled the 'Britannias'.

To look at they were rather on the ugly side, it is true. Their boilers were pitched so high as almost to leave no room for chimney or dome; their huge outside cylinders tilted down towards the central coupled axle, the balance weights of whose wheels came right inwards to meet the hubs; and all the moving parts were shamelessly external. As with the already described Great Eastern 'Decapod', the central driving wheels of this 'Decapod-plus-two' were flangeless, and those on either side had thinned flanges, to facilitate the negotiation of curves. They had wide fireboxes, though these had to be accommodated over the rear pair of coupled wheels and so were less deep than those of the 'Pacifics'. Many of their components had to be non-standard. Some had single chimneys, some double; others had various extra devices attached. A few for a while were given mechanical stokers, but these, though popular with their crews, and able to deal with poor quality coal, pushed too much of it into the firebox, so that they were eventually removed.

Above *Preserved BR Standard 2-10-0 No 92220* Evening Star *at the head of a special train.* (LCGB)

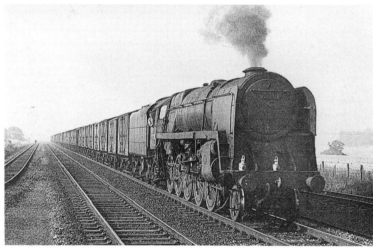

Right *BR Standard 2-10-0 No 92201 on a fast freight train.* (LCGB)

Their haulage capacity was colossal. To give an example, on the Somerset & Dorset line between Bath and Bournemouth some of them were drafted to work passenger trains, including the prestigious 'Pines Express' during 1960–1962. This line, which crosses the Mendip Hills, had fearsome gradients on either side of the summit, with long stretches at 1 in 50 in either direction, and passenger trains of any weight had to be double-headed. The Class '9s' kept time unassisted with any load they were given, full-throatedly attacking the banks, their drivers knowing they could safely mortgage their boilers and then recover pressure after the summit had been passed.

This was one kind of achievement; another was the unexpected ability to run fast on passenger trains, though this did not often happen as the authorities frowned on the practice. Once, when there was a shortage of motive power on the East Coast Main Line on a summer

Saturday, No 92184 had to deputize for the usually available 4-6-2 on the afternoon 'Heart of Midlothian' express from Edinburgh to King's Cross, taking over at Grantham. It proceeded to gain time and actually passed Hatfield 6 minutes early, having reached 90 miles an hour coming down from Stoke summit and 78 twice on level stretches south of Peterborough — this with wheels only 5 feet in diameter, and without any overheating! Patrick Stirling, who consistently gave all his express locomotives single driving wheels (because, as he put it, an engine with coupled wheels trying to go fast was 'like a laddie running wi' his breeks doun') would have been astounded at this thoroughgoing refutation of his dogma. None of the single drivers built by him was ever recorded as attaining 90 miles an hour.

The qualities and abilities of the Class '9's have been emphasized in view of frequent attempts to make them better still. One can scarcely speak of attempting to gild the lily, but perhaps a suitable metaphor would be that of burnishing a black tulip. As many as 251 of these engines were built, and on some of them devices were tried out which might make them better than best, so far as economy in working was concerned. Two of the more interesting experiments — one involving a very considerable alteration in design — are described below.

Quite early after the building of the Standard range of locomotives had begun, it was decided to fit ten freight locomotives with Franco-Crosti boilers. Riddles and his colleagues were anxious to see whether the claims made for this device could be achieved in practice under British conditions. The Franco-Crosti boiler was an Italian invention which aimed to make a more thorough use of the hot gases of combustion after they had passed through the boiler tubes. In conventional locomotives they were simply caught up with the exhaust steam and expelled, still hot, to the atmosphere. Previous designers had pondered, and sometimes devised, ways of using that wasted heat; Bulleid, as we have seen, was one. Dr Crosti's method was to bring the hot gases, after they had emerged from the boiler tubes, back through another system, or systems, of tubes which traversed a pre-heater, or pre-heaters, which contained feed water drawn from the tender supply, to which they gave up their remaining heat. At the same time the exhaust steam from the cylinders, passing through a jacket enclosing each pre-heater, also gave up heat to the feed water before exhausting itself through blast pipes. What would otherwise have been the smokebox, in a Crosti engine became simply a place where the gases of combustion reversed direction; it was totally enclosed and had no chimney.

The real smokebox was a chamber below the rear part of the boiler. Here the exhaust steam passed out through a row of blast pipe nozzles to one side of the boiler, reaching the atmosphere through an elongated side chimney and sucking the greatly cooled gases of combustion with it as it expelled itself. The feed water pre-heater or pre-heaters received water through injectors from below and to the rear, which made its way between the heating elements, its temperature gradually rising, and being forced upwards by the water that entered behind it; eventually it passed through clack valves into the boiler itself, being now almost at boiling point. Once there, and in contact with the fire tubes and firebox sides and crown, it boiled rapidly. A credit point for this system was that a smaller boiler could be provided than would otherwise have been necessary, since instead of having to do the whole work of producing steam it only had to finish the operation. A debit point, however, was that the exhaust had to leave the cylinders at higher pressure than would otherwise have been necessary, since it had to exert a smokebox vacuum strong enough to draw the firebox gases through two sets of tubes instead of only one.

Dr Crosti's locomotives, as used on the Italian State Railways, were rebuilds which had a pre-heater drum on either side of their boilers and whose chimneys had been removed. The larger loading gauge allowed this; the smaller British one would not. Nevertheless, he believed his system was universally applicable and naturally welcomed the news that British Railways proposed to build ten of their new freight engines on this pattern. His invention had been patented and British Railways recognized that he was entitled to remuneration, but they were careful about the agreement they made. A contract was eventually agreed by which the full royalty would be paid if the system, applied to a Class '9' 2-10-0, brought about an 18 per cent economy in fuel over that consumed by a similar locomotive conventionally built in pre-determined conditions of working. If the percentage economy were less, the royalty would be less, and if under 12 per cent none would be due at all. Crosti was quite sure that the expected economies would be achieved.

One thing, however, seems to have been overlooked at the time. If an existing locomotive, whose efficiency had lessened with age, were fitted with a new device to improve its performance, it might very well show considerable improvement simply because large parts of it had been renewed. This would have been the case, no doubt, with the reconstructed engines working in Italy, France and Germany. British Railways, however, were going to match a *new* Franco-Crosti engine against a new one of conventional type. This was no doubt a fairer way to make a comparison, but it weighted the scales against Crosti.

The ten modified 2-10-0s emerged from Crewe works in 1955. Each differed from the Crosti engines on the Continent in having only *one* pre-heater, a long drum placed along the centre line of the engine below a boiler of somewhat reduced size. To the eye it appeared to have a front smokebox and chimney, but appearances were deceptive. When the engine had to be lit up, the 'chimney' was used to provide a draught for the fire, but once steam had been raised its top was closed and the

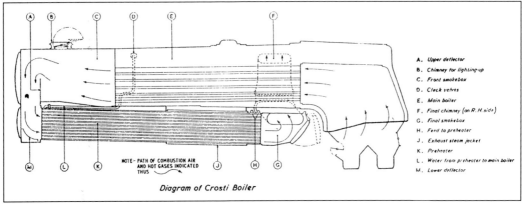

A. Upper deflector
B. Chimney for lighting-up
C. Front smokebox
D. Clack valves
E. Main boiler
F. Final chimney (on R.H. side)
G. Final smokebox
H. Feed to preheater
J. Exhaust steam jacket
K. Preheater
L. Water from preheater to main boiler
M. Lower deflector

NOTE – PATH OF COMBUSTION AIR AND HOT GASES INDICATED THUS

Diagram of Crosti Boiler

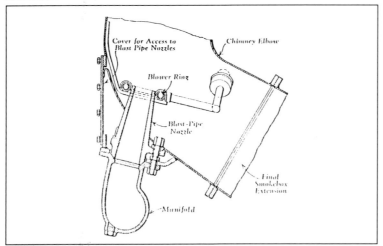

Cover for Access to Blast Pipe Nozzles

Chimney Elbow

Blower Ring

Blast-Pipe Nozzle

Final Smokebox Extension

Manifold

Above *Diagram of the Franco-Crosti boiler as used on the ten Class '9' 2-10-0s built on this pattern for British Railways, showing the path of the gases from the firebox, first through the boiler and then through the pre-heater before being expelled through the side chimney. (Railway Magazine)*

Left *Cross-section of the lower part of the side chimney on the Franco-Crosti 2-10-0, showing the relative positions of the nozzles (of which there were four arranged longitudinally) which ejected the exhaust steam, and the final extension of the smokebox. (Railway Magazine)*

Left *Right-hand view of a rather grubby Franco-Crosti 2-10-0, showing the side chimney screened by a metal plate, from which the final exhaust emerged. (NRM)*

apparent smokebox became an intermediate gas and smoke receiver. The single pre-heater received the firebox gases into its tubes and took them back to the real smokebox, which was just ahead of and below the lower part of the firebox throatplate. Around the rear of the pre-heater was the jacket that received exhaust steam from the cylinders, and from it the steam then passed to a row of blast pipes which, within the irregularly-shaped smokebox cavity, pointed upwards on the right-hand side of the boiler towards an elongated chimney behind a flat shield, whose top was at about the level of the right-hand spectacle glass and several feet ahead of it. The force of the emitted steam caused the partial vacuum sufficient to draw the hot gases through both sets of tubes and so into the atmosphere. The whole arrangement fitted neatly within the

British loading gauge. Seen from in front, the circular door of the pre-heater was clearly visible; from the side of the locomotive the only prominent 'give-away' features were the bulging cases above the cylinders which covered the piping that took the exhaust steam to the jacket, and (from the right) the flat casing which hid the true chimney.

Soon after being built, one of the Crostis was matched at the Rugby testing plant against a non-Crosti standard 2–10–0, with a sustained evaporation rate of 16,000 lbs of water per hour and a firing rate of up to 2,000 lbs of coal an hour. The expected economies were not realized. Later actual road tests were undertaken, the contenders being Crosti No 92023 and unmodified engine No 92050. The first ran on 9 and 10 November, the second on 8 and 9 December. Each locomotive hauled a 600-ton load of coaching stock, including a dynamometer car. The chosen stretch of line was between Carlisle and Hurlford, along the former Glasgow & South Western main line. Specified constant steaming rates were kept to as far as possible where the line was level or uphill; elsewhere the drivers were asked to keep the speed to between 45 and 50 miles an hour by the use of the brake. To make the tests represent service conditions as much as possible (when freight trains usually have to make intermediate halts) 10-minute stops were arranged at Dumfries, Carronbridge and New Cumnock in both directions, while at Hurlford each train waited for two hours before returning. In the dynamometer car the work done in hauling the train and the water and coal consumptions were measured, the amount used in lighting up being added to the latter.

Engine	Date	Load (tons)	Running time (mins)	Standing time (mins)	Total work done (HP hrs)	Total coal used (cwts)	Average coal (lbs per DBHP hour)
Crosti	9/11/55	604	287	269	2,610	93	3.99
Crosti	10/11/55	604	286	266	2,616	93	3.98
Standard	8/12/55	601	291	282	2,683	101	4.37
Standard	9/12/55	601[a]	297	341	3,038	106	3.91

a   571 tons from Dumfries to Carlisle. A defective vehicle had to be detached at Dumfries.
Note: Average calorific value of coal: Crosti locomotive — 12,450 BTU/lb; Standard locomotive — 12,200 BTU/lb

The table shows the results of these tests. The Crosti engine had somewhat the better of them. However, it had been agreed beforehand that it had to show at least 12 per cent advantage for any royalties to be payable at all. In the words of the Official Report:

'Taking the mean of the two tests with each engine, and correcting for the different calorific values of the coal used, the saving of the Crosti over the Standard in total coal used was 7.9 per cent, and in coal per DBHP hour 1.7 per cent. It will be seen, however, that the second test with the Standard engine was not strictly comparable with the other tests, as considerably more work was done by the engine and the standing time was longer. It is suggested that a better comparison is obtained from the results of the two Crosti tests and the first Standard engine test. In this case the saving in total coal used becomes 6.1 per cent, and in coal per DBHP hour 7 per cent. Over the range of workings concerned, the boiler efficiency values obtained on the constant speed road tests were approximately 1 per cent better in the case of the Crosti and 2 per cent worse in the case of the Standard, as compared with Rugby. That is to say, the road tests indicated a difference in boiler efficiency of approximately 8 per cent in favour of the Crosti. However, for the conditions of speed and steam rate involved in the tests with the 600-ton train, the drawbar power for the Crosti engine, as derived from the constant speed road tests, would be approximately 6 per cent less. The net result is that the Crosti engine would show a saving in coal of the order of 4 per cent.'

Dr Crosti himself was surprised and even incredulous when told of the results, for they seemed quite out of keeping with what had happened in Italy. Arbitration was sought; the test results were submitted to the celebrated French locomotive engineer André Chapelon and his comments were invited. They took some time to arrive and, though extensive, were non-committal. British Railways and the firm which Crosti headed in Milan then struck a deal; an *ex gratia* payment was made to the Italians, who agreed to let the matter rest.

By this time, 1957, the end of steam in Great Britain was already in sight, and the ten Crosti engines were in the bad books both of the men who had to drive them and of their owners. The objections of the footplate crews arose from the positioning of the side chimney, which belched out fumes and steam so close to the cab that the forward view from the right-hand window was often completely obscured and the cab interior became intolerably dirty and smelly from the smoke which invaded it. British Railways' objection was that the system was actually damaging the locomotives' structure. The gases of combustion, being so much cooler than normal when reaching the smokebox, were depositing sulphuric acid there, which in the ordinary way would have been exhausted as sulphur dioxide into the atmosphere. (To put it another way, the engines were keeping their environmental pollution to themselves!). The smokeboxes and chimneys were being eroded to such an extent that it was decided to rebuild all ten locomotives as conventionally operating machines. The small boilers were retained but the pre-heater drums and smokeboxes were removed, and the intermediate gas receiver with its false chimney was replaced by a real smokebox with a true chimney through which steam exhausted through a blast pipe nozzle placed in the customary position. For the remainder of their short lives the engines were driven in the usual way, though their smaller boilers restricted their sphere of operation as they could not now cope with the heaviest loads.

The second device which British Railways tried out on a Class '9' engine was the Giesl ejector. Dr Giesl-Gieslingen, a senior engineer on the staff of the Vienna Locomotive Works at Florisdorf, Austria, had spent many years studying the phenomenon of the steam locomotive's exhaust before coming out with his invention. In the days of George Stephenson, and for many years afterwards, the practice was to exhaust steam from the cylinders through a round nozzle directed towards a chimney immediately above, whose inner section was also round and tapered slightly upwards and outwards. The force of the expelled steam caused a certain degree of vacuum within the smokebox. Nature, as the philosophers used to tell us in their picturesque manner, abhors a vacuum. It had to be filled from somewhere, and this could only be with the hot gases from the firebox sucked through the boiler tubes, which heated the boiler water on the way. In the inter-war years a number of variations on the time-honoured round-nozzle blast pipe and round chimney were tried. One was the Kylchap system, which used a double exhaust through a pair of blast pipes, with a double chimney above. Another was the Lemaitre multiple jet blast, a ring of nozzles which exhausted through a widened chimney. The Giesl system was the last in the line of these draughting experiments, and proved very advantageous in Austria and other European countries. When tried out in Great Britain, however, it did not appear to be so strikingly successful as to warrant continuance. A certain amount of controversy was created in consequence, and British Railways was accused of dragging its feet and losing an opportunity to make significant economies — as related below.

In the Giesl method, the blast orifices were arranged not in a pair or a ring but in a longitudinal row of seven, one behind the other. Their total cross-sectional area was not greater than it would have been using any previously tried method. They exhausted steam through a narrow oblong chimney whose slot-like orifice, widening out from the base upwards, was immediately above the blast pipes. Their vacuum-creating effect proved in practice to be greater than any former method could produce. So a stronger draught was created, the fire in the firebox

A Franco-Crosti 2-10-0 hauling a heavy goods train. Note that the exhaust is not escaping from the front chimney (which has been sealed within) but from the side chimney which is immediately behind the dome on the far side. (NRM)

burned brighter and more effectively, and better combustion of the coal was effected.

Furthermore, along with the increased draught which the Giesl system caused, another improvement was associated. The front extremities of the lower tubes in the boiler were narrowed. This had the double effect of causing the gases of combustion to emerge into the smokebox faster, so that when meeting the upward blast from the cylinders they could (so to speak) more readily attach themselves to it, and also (because of the restricted openings at the forward ends of the lower pipes) the gases passing through the tubes in the upper pipes, in contact with the superheater elements, came through with more force and superheated the steam more thoroughly before it went to do its work in the cylinders. The full Giesl system was therefore a double one; it modified the shape of the blast and it boosted the superheat.

Dr Giesl believed that the installation of his system in any conventionally draughted locomotive would so greatly increase the economy in working that it would pay for itself in a year, or even less. Not only coal but also water consumption would be greatly lowered. He also maintained (and this is what specially interested British Railways) that low-grade coal could be used if a suitable spark arrestor could be fitted, and he had devised one in which the upper parts of the blast pipes and the lower part of the oblong chimney were encased in a wire cage.

British Railways were surprisingly slow to recognize the potentialities of the Giesl ejector. They were not alone in their scepticism about something that seemed too good to be true, but their unbelief persisted longer than that of the Continental lines which had one by one accepted it. What finally persuaded the Railway Executive to give it a trial was its possible relevance to the use of poor quality coal. The National Coal Board had a great deal of this to dispose of and was only too anxious that British Railways should take as much of it as possible off their hands — at, of course, a reduced price. Coal with excessive slack was unsuitable for burning in a locomotive of normal design, because so much went up the chimney unburned. Introduced loose into the firebox, it tended to be caught up in the draught before being ignited. In 1959, the year after No 92250 had been built, it was accordingly fitted with a Giesl ejector in place of its previously installed double blast pipe and chimney, and tests were made with it at Rugby. These were thorough, and aimed to ensure a satisfactory comparison with other similar engines not thus modified. In particular it was desired to find out how the engine would perform on coal which was far below the quality of the basic 'Grade B' Blidworth which was used as a standard of comparison whenever a British Railways steam locomotive was tested. Giesl himself came to observe the tests.

The results showed that the Giesl system had rather more than twice the vacuum-creating capacity of a conventional exhaust system, and that at a medium rate of working it showed a fuel saving of 4½ per cent. It also demonstrated an ability to cause good steaming when the coal used was of a kind hitherto deemed unusable. It was naturally speculated that if this could happen in a locomotive which was the most efficient type British Railways possessed, much more advantage could be obtained if other types were similarly equipped. However, with one solitary exception, to be mentioned below, no more locomotives were Giesl-fitted. It remains to ask why not.

In the case of the Crosti engines, a saving of not less than 12 per cent had been insisted on, else no royalties would be payable; in fact, the actual saving had been a great deal less than that. Broadly speaking, the case was the same with No 92250. A saving of 4½ per cent was felt to be nothing like enough. As to the possibility of using poor coal, here British Railways' reaction was more favourable, but whatever good intentions they had foundered on an unexpected reef. Bargaining with the National Coal Board failed to elicit from them a price for the poorest type of coal which was usable, which the BR considered low enough. The upshot was that no futher 2–10–0s were fitted with Giesl ejectors. Dr Giesl was extremely disappointed, and considered that the reasons British Railways advanced — that the price difference between good coal and the poorest that was actually possible to use when a Giesl ejector was employed was not great enough, that whatever economies were shown during the tests would be halved in normal service, and that steam locomotives were being phased out of primary duties in any case — were mere excuses. They certainly do not seem sufficient in themselves to warrant rejection of a device which, applied to a large number of engines, would have paid for itself many times over before the last steam locomotive went to the scrapyard. Was this just another example of adherence to 'old-time religion?'

Class '9' 2-10-0 No 92250, the only example of this class to be fitted with the Giesl ejector. The typical long narrow chimney can be clearly seen. (NRM)

However, their story was not quite finished. On the Southern Railway,

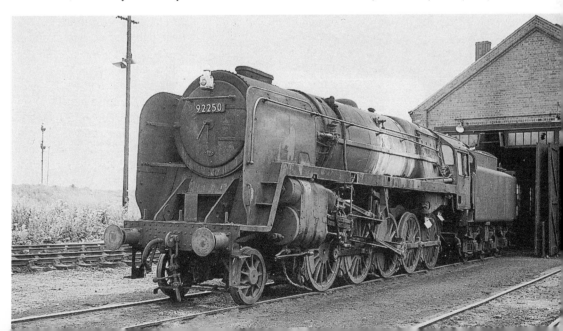

British Railways (Southern Region) light 'Pacific' of the 'Battle of Britain' Class, No 34064 Fighter Command, which was fitted with a Giesl ejector in 1962 and then showed itself able to match the 'Merchant Navy' 'Pacifics' in performance. The narrow chimney can be seen against the sky under the smoke deflector. (NRM)

those 'Pacifics' that Bulleid had built which had not yet been modified — that is, about half of the 'West Country' and 'Battle of Britain' Classes — were causing trouble by ejecting sparks and starting fires, not only along the sides of the tracks but among growing crops in adjacent fields. The fitting of spark-arrestors to them unbalanced the draughting. It occurred to those in command at Brighton works that the fitting of a Giesl ejector might solve the problem, and authority was obtained to do this. It was the ability of the wire cage around the exhaust jets to hold back sparks which suggested the change, but in fact its fitting had the beneficent effects of lowering the fuel consumption and increasing the engine's pulling power at the same time, so that it performed work up to 'Merchant Navy' standards. The locomotive concerned, No 34064 *Fighter Command*, showed itself fully able to manage the newly accelerated Bournemouth expresses, while keeping its sparks to itself. It was an indication of what would have been possible on other main lines. However, this was done in 1962, when steam was only four years from extinction. The patient was already breathing its last and the 'No Resuscitation' sign had already been displayed.

23

Could there be a return of steam?

On the face of it, a revival of the steam locomotive on British Rail would seem as unlikely as the return of the stage-coach to our roads, or the issue of longbows to regiments of the British Army. At its best it was not an efficient user of fuel. It was convenient to use it when the only alternative was electrification, whose first cost was enormously expensive, and which never presented itself as a main-line possibility to any of the pre-grouping railways. Later, when the possibility of diesel traction began to appear, what deterred the Big Four from doing more than a little experimenting was the fact that oil had to be imported from the Middle East; coal, on the other hand, was on their doorsteps, for each of them had one or more coalfields adjacent to its system. During the 'thirties the Southern Railway's management made a start on main-line electrification, and before the Second World War broke out the South Coast between Hastings and Portsmouth was linked with the capital by fast and frequent electric trains, the steam locomotive being elbowed out by degrees. But it was still the recognized mode of haulage over by far the greater part of the country, and where we should have been without it during the war years, Heaven only knows.

With the return of peace, things began to change. Affluence spread in greater or lesser degree to almost everyone, and this showed itself in changed travel patterns. The huge growth of private car ownership, even in urban areas where public transport was plentiful, made people in general more mobile. Strangely this does not seem to have been at the expense of the railways. Main-line passenger traffic increased, though many branch lines sickened and died — or were given a lethal injection by Dr Beeching. The habit of travel, by whatever means, had increased. It is instructive to compare the pattern of daily express train services between London and any one of the chief provincial towns during 1939 with what that pattern is now. In almost every case the service is faster and more frequent. Increased demand has also made one mainline electrification scheme after another profitable. It cannot be long before electric express trains will have ousted diesel-hauled trains on all main lines — just as the latter ousted steam trains during the 'fifties and 'sixties. The latter could not have coped with the demands for quick inter-city transport which the diesel-electric locomotives, from the now vanished 'Deltics' downwards, have shown themselves able to satisfy. Moreover, the steam locomotive's chief asset, of being able to use indigenous fuel, disappeared when North Sea oil began to be exploited. In its Stephensonian form it was environmentally undesirable, distributing noxious and sulphurous fumes into the air. (The same objection, however, applies to its rival). As known in the 'sixties, it had to go.

However, though it could never again have the monopoly it enjoyed in the past, it could like Arthur be a 'once and future king', though reigning over a much reduced territory. A case can be made out for it as an auxiliary mode of traction for freight traffic. There are always going to be some lines which will not be worth electrifying, and there is also the uneasy awareness that North Sea oil will not last for ever. Coal, on the other hand, will still be there, and new collieries take the places of those which are worked out. The factor that favoured steam in the past may favour it yet again.

It would not seem environmentally acceptable that coal should be burned in locomotive fireboxes as in the past. The beautiful columns of black smoke and steam which so delighted railway photographers in the past exacted payment from innumerable sufferers from bronchitis and pneumonia. But first steam locomotives ran on coke, and so could the last ones, emitting no longer the sulphurous and tormenting fumes which troubled the ghost of Hamlet's father, but just carbon dioxide and water vapour. Like North Sea oil, North Sea gas will one day become exhausted and coal gas will probably have to be manufactured once more. There should then be plenty of coke, some of which could be earmarked for railway locomotion.

Another possibility is the burning of waste oil, which should not at any rate be *more* environmentally damaging if burned in locomotive fireboxes than if burned anywhere else. Innumerable cars go daily to countless garages for oil-changing. In the village in Nottinghamshire where I lived 20 years ago, the warmest spot during the winter was the local garage, whose proprietor collected the contents of car sumps and burned them in a stove; it cost him nothing. A little organization and the same thing could be done in steam locomotive fireboxes. Indeed, the Great Eastern Railway was doing something like this a hundred years ago; the celebrated 4–2–2 singles built by James Holden in a number of cases burned waste oil from Stratford works.

Finally, there is turf, which can be dug from peat beds all over the Scottish Highlands; Bulleid showed it could be done successfully in Ireland, and developed the kind of engine which could be built here. Turf is perhaps the most benign of all fuels; it does no damage to the environment, and it even smells good. Deep mines are not needed; peats are cut in the open and the operation is at least as healthy as that of the forestry worker.

What would the New Model Army of steam locomotives resemble? They might well look much the same as the smaller Standard locomotives that British Railways produced in the 'fifties. The author confesses to a wish that there might also be a sprinkling of Bulleid's 'Q1's. The design would be tailored to suit whatever fuel was most readily obtainable. With coke or oil fuel, no doubt one-man operation would be possible if the firing could be done automatically, but two men would probably be needed with a turf-burner.

On what routes might such locomotives be expected to run? Some lines suggest themselves: Newcastle to Carlisle; Carlisle to Barrow and Carnforth; Carnforth to Leeds and Bradford; the old Lancashire & Yorkshire route across the Pennines; most of the lines in Lincolnshire; Peterborough to Ely and Norwich; Crewe to Cardiff; South-west Wales beyond Swansea; the mid-Wales lines; Exeter to Barnstaple; Westbury to Weymouth. In Scotland: the West Highland line to Oban and Mallaig; Aberdeen to Inverness; everything north and west of Inverness. Here steam could handle the freight traffic — and maybe, if diesel oil becomes ruinously expensive, the present admirable Sprinter services might have to give way to steam railcars for the handful of passengers. One can indulge one's fancy *ad libitum*. It probably won't happen, but it *could* happen. That would be the final experiment with steam — to bring it back again.

Index